Animal Morphogenesis

Electron micrograph of the fertilized human ovum showing male and female pronuclei. The zygote was recovered from the oviduct during an operation performed twenty-six hours after sexual intercourse. [From L. Zamboni et al., in *J. Cell Biol.*, 30:579–600, 1966. By permission of Dr. Zamboni and The Rockefeller University Press.]

Volumes in This Series:

Algae and Fungi
C. J. Alexopoulos and H. C. Bold, The University of Texas

Sensory Mechanisms
James Case, University of California, Santa Barbara

Integral Animal Behavior
David E. Davis, The Pennsylvania State University

Molecular Genetics
A. Gib DeBusk, Florida State University

Biology of Higher Cryptogams
William T. Doyle, University of California, Santa Cruz

Viruses and Molecular Biology
Dean Fraser, Indiana University

Hormonal Control in Vertebrates
B. E. Frye, The University of Michigan

Cells and Energy
Richard A. Goldsby, Yale University

The Physiology of Cells
Karl F. Guthe, The University of Michigan

Process and Pattern in Evolution
Terrell H. Hamilton, The University of Texas

Tools of Biology
Edward S. Lenhoff, Harvard University

A Biology of Lower Invertebrates
W. D. Russell-Hunter, Syracuse University

Animal Morphogenesis
John W. Saunders, Jr., State University of New York, Albany

Evolution and Systematics
Otto T. Solbrig, The University of Michigan

Development in Flowering Plants
John G. Torrey, Harvard University

Principles of Development and Differentiation
C. H. Waddington, University of Edinburgh

Additional Volumes in Preparation

CURRENT CONCEPTS IN BIOLOGY

A Macmillan Series

NORMAN H. GILES, WALTER KENWORTHY, JOHN G. TORREY, Editors

Animal Morphogenesis

John W. Saunders, Jr.

State University of New York and The Marine Biological Laboratory

The Macmillan Company, New York
Collier-Macmillan Limited, London

To Miss Bess
with respect, affection, and gratitude

The Macmillan Company, New York

Collier-Macmillan Canada, Ltd., Toronto, Ontario

Printed in the United States of America

Preface

THIS BOOK is about animal eggs and embryos, where they come from, and how they develop into functional organisms. It is hoped that it will help college students and others who have begun to study biology to learn some of the basic facts and ideas of animal development in a modern context.

One of my reasons for writing this book is that at the present time the conceptual framework of developmental biology is being rejuvenated and fructified by the exciting synthesis of molecular genetics and classical embryology. A few years ago, biologists studying embryos were concerned chiefly with describing developmental events that could be detected grossly or by means of simple optical devices, and with experimentally analyzing the causal connections between these events—they conducted the kinds of studies called "developmental mechanics" and "developmental physiology." Now, however, stimulated by new insights gained from genetics and biochemistry, we are increasingly concerned with questions about the basic chemical mechanisms that underlie the behavior of the genes and their control of the synthesis of specific macromolecules characteristic of a cell's state of differentiation. For example, how, when, and where do the genes determine what proteins shall be synthesized during development? How are the proteins assembled into the structural elements of cells, tissues, and organs?

We may formulate these and similar questions in the abstract and then seek their answers in whatever organisms seem most likely to reveal them—bacteria, bacteriophages, yeasts, algae, sea urchins, and so on. The molecular approach using model systems has been spectacularly rewarding to researchers, as this book should indicate. Indeed, it has been so rewarding that there is some concern that the student will be so caught up in the current excitement about the molecular biology of development that he will neglect the abundant descriptive material

v

upon which the molecular biologist ultimately must draw to make further gains. More importantly, there is concern that he will remain relatively unaware of the magnificent fabric of developmental principles that has been woven from the discoveries of classical embryologists of an earlier era and that serves to bring a kind of order and meaning to developmental knowledge unattainable through an approach limited to the molecular level.

On the other hand, there is also cause for concern in the reluctance of many students, and even of some teachers, to come to grips with those aspects of the biology of development that can be approached only by the molecular route. For some, this reluctance may stem from an unwarranted fear of becoming involved in problems involving biophysics and biochemistry. For others, it may derive from a reluctance, perhaps not formulated or articulated, to see the supposed mysteries of life fall to the assault of exact science.

It is hoped that this book will assist in overcoming these concerns and that it will contribute to the achievement of a view wherein factual and conceptual knowledge of development at all levels—from molecular to organismic—can be perceived in proper balance and perspective by students with varied backgrounds and interests. There is no exhaustive presentation of the facts of development, but its chief outlines in several animal forms are offered; there is considerable emphasis on the principles that unify and give a higher order of meaning to the factual matter; the molecular aspects of development are given a treatment that is representative of the more significant trends in today's thinking.

The book is intended to help students who are taking their first college course in biology or zoology gain a modern, yet simplified, assessment of the biology of development. It conceivably could be used by high school students of advanced standing for special reading; and it would serve as an outline textbook for a first college course in embryology if properly supplemented by a lecture series.

I have assumed that prospective readers will have an elementary biological vocabulary applicable to anatomy and physiology at levels from cell to organ and some knowledge of Mendelian genetics. Thus the book will offer relatively few new terms. But when words appear that may be new to the reader or that are key words for understanding, they are presented in italics. Terms so introduced will be defined, or their meanings will emerge from the various contexts in which they appear.

Hopefully, some students will be encouraged to pursue further some of the topics introduced in this book. Many references to texts and to the original scientific literature may be found in the captions accompanying the illustrations. Also, a list of sources for further reading is presented at the end of the book. Most of the references are to textbooks and semipopular accounts, but a few are to technical articles, so the reader may pursue his interests to whatever level of sophistication he wishes.

I am particularly grateful to generous colleagues who provided photographs for reproduction in this work. Their specific contributions are credited in the captions accompanying the figures. Special thanks go to Peter Loewer for his artistry and accuracy in executing the drawings. I am indebted to my wife, Lilyan C. Saunders, who tested parts of the manuscript for its pedagogic effectiveness in her classroom, and to John F. Fallon, who provided some original drawings and contributed helpful discussions and critical comments. Fred Wilt offered careful and constructive criticism of the entire manuscript, and I am grateful for his help.

J. W. S., Jr.

Contents

1

Introduction   1

Problem of the Egg / Problem of the Student

2

Origin of the Fertilized Egg   4

Gametes / Fertilization

3

Sorting the Materials of the Egg: Formation of Germ Layers   19

Cleavage and Gastrulation

4

Morphogenetic Processes   40

Ectoderm / Mesoderm / Endoderm

5

Principles of Development: The Conceptual Framework for Developmental Events   51

Differentiation / Determination / Dependent Differentiation: Induction / Genetic Limitations / Reciprocal Action / The Morphogenetic Field / Preformation and Epigenesis

6

Genetic Control of Development   71

Nuclear Determination of Developmental Events / The Genetic Code and How to Translate It / Control of Genetic Readout during Development: Today's Challenge / Epigenetic Control of Morphogenesis: The Challenge for Tomorrow

Selected References   111

Index   114

Introduction

IN MOST LIVING THINGS a new generation begins with the fertilized egg, or *zygote*, a cell formed by the union of the ovum from the female parent and the sperm from the male (see cover illustration). The word *zygote*, derived from Greek, means yoked or joined together, reminding us that each of the parents has a role in determining the characteristics of the new individual—its size, shape, physiological attributes, behavioral patterns, and so on. The totality of the process whereby these characteristics are achieved and their changes throughout adulthood and senescence, eventually leading to death, we call *development*. The structural features that the organism acquires—those relating to its size and shape and the construction of its cells, tissues, and organs—collectively comprise the *form* of the organism. The study of form is called *morphology;* the sum of the processes whereby form is developed is *morphogenesis*.

This volume deals with the way in which the form and function of the organism develop from the fertilized egg. It is almost entirely about the morphogenesis of animals, and it treats the period of development that occurs before birth or hatching, with emphasis on the description of early morphogenetic events and the mechanisms that control them at various levels of organization, from the gross to the molecular.

Problem of the Egg

The problem that confronts the fertilized egg is formidable. A cell no more than tens of microns in diameter, as a rule, must become an organism comprising perhaps tens of trillions of cells. But more than this, these trillions of cells must be many different kinds, there must be

1

just the right number and proportion of each kind, and they must be assembled in the correct geometry. Cells must be arranged into tissues and tissues into organs, and the organs must be aligned into organ systems—the digestive system, the nervous system, and so on—to carry out complex tasks.

The magnitude of the egg's problem may be appreciated by noting some of the kinds of cells that it must manufacture in the embryo of a vertebrate. They include muscle cells, which produce the contractile proteins, move the skeletal framework, pump the blood, and propel material through the digestive tract, and connective-tissue cells such as fibroblasts, which synthesize collagen and other tough protein fibrils that lace the various other cells together into tissues and organs. They also include red blood cells, manufacturers of hemoglobin, which transports oxygen to the tissues, and liver cells, which, among other activities, manufacture serum proteins and bile They include cells that secrete mucoprotein and line the digestive tract; other cells associated with the digestive tract that synthesize and secrete the enzymes that catalyze the hydrolysis of the food; and cells of the various endocrine organs, whose protein or steroid hormones are transported by the blood to affect target organs elsewhere in the body.

The great variety of cells and tissues and the intricate ways they are woven to form organs and organ systems point up clearly that the developing organism must contain a master plan, or blueprint, for their construction. This master plan is the *genome,* the endowment of genes brought to the zygote by the nuclei of egg and sperm; it is present in each cell of the new individual. During development, mechanisms must be set in motion according to this master plan to control the multiplication of cells, the formation of different kinds of cells, and their organization into functional units. The egg has the problem of reading its genetic blueprint, and following the instructions it provides.

Problem of the Student

The egg has solved *its* problem. Almost without fail each egg produced in the right environment does form a new individual that, in turn, makes sperm or eggs that contribute another generation. The problem that confronts us as students of development is to learn how the egg does it. For a good while at least, this problem will not be solved as satisfactorily as we should like; but a beginning can be made by asking appropriate questions of the developing system. Properly presented to the embryo, these questions elicit answers that tell something about development and suggest further questions that then enable us to penetrate more deeply into the underlying events.

A good procedure in any investigation is to ask simple questions that can be answered by means of direct observation, aided perhaps by simple tools. Thereafter, as one gains understanding, he can ask more complex questions whose answers require observations under more rigorous conditions and the application of a more sophisticated technology. This general approach will guide us in this book. The first step is to ask what the sequence of major descriptive events in development is—those events that can be seen with the unaided eye or with relatively simple lenses or microscopes. The answer to this question is a schedule of the major changes that occur from fertilization to birth.

Next, what are the causal relationships between these major events? In order to formulate questions about causality, we shall bring into play insights gained from observing the sequence and pattern of these major events. And we shall seek answers related to mechanisms that operate in the progressive unfolding of the body plan—mechanisms observable principally in the structuring of tissues and organs.

Underlying all morphogenetic changes, of course, are events that occur at the cellular and molecular levels of organizations, and so we shall finally turn to questions about the differences between kinds of cells and the ways in which these differences arise under the control of the hereditary material, the genes.

In a limited amount of time, it is impossible for the student to learn a great deal about the development of even one organism, much less the wealth of detail that is known about the developmental histories of many organisms. Nor is it possible for the student to review the numerous analytic studies that have been made concerning the integration and control of developmental events. But a great deal of detailed knowledge is not necessary in order to have a significant understanding of development. What is important is that one gain sufficient knowledge of the facts of development to be able to induce meaningful generalizations about them. These generalizations will provide a conceptual framework into which additional facts may be fitted as they are acquired and will offer a starting point for the formulation of questions designed to produce an ever more penetrating insight into the nature of development.

In sum, it is hoped that as the student pursues this account he will learn something of the facts of animal development at various levels of embryonic organization; that he will come to some understanding of the kinds of mechanisms that bring about morphogenetic events at various levels of organization; and finally, that he will gain an appreciation of the major concepts that give unity to existing knowledge and that point the way toward acquisition of further knowledge and new conceptual insights.

2

Origin of the Fertilized Egg

THERE IS NO discontinuity of life between generations—between parent and offspring—for the new life arises from cells (egg and sperm) that are descended from the fertilized eggs that produced the parental generation. We shall now make it our task to see how the reproductive cells are formed from parental tissues and what endowment they bring to their union at the time of fertilization.

Gametes

The eggs and sperm are called *germ cells* or *gametes*. They originate in the gonads—ovary and testis in female and male, respectively—from a relatively few *primordial germ cells* that were set aside during rather early stages in the development of the parental generation (see Chapter 4). Through multiplication, the primordial germ cells form a population of special cells, the *gonial cells,* that are called *oögonia* in the female and *spermatogonia* in the male.

The gonial cells are similar in both sexes. They are often somewhat larger than other cells and have a large ovoid or rounded nucleus with prominent masses of chromatin. The cytoplasm contains the usual organelles with which students of biology are familiar: mitochondria, which comprise the principal energy-transforming apparatus of the cell; endoplasmic reticulum, studded with ribosomes, which are the sites of protein synthesis (see Chapter 6); Golgi apparatus, which probably serves to package proteins; and centrioles, which function in cell division.

The multiplication of the gonial cells is accomplished through mitotic cell division (Figure 2·1). It is not necessary to review mitosis

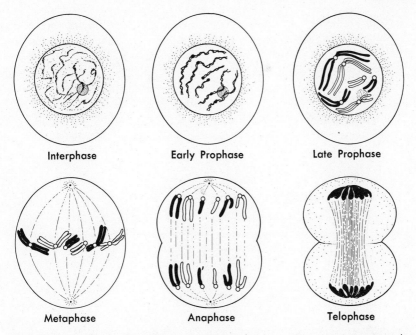

Interphase   Early Prophase   Late Prophase

Metaphase   Anaphase   Telophase

Figure 2·1. Mitotic cell division. Six chromosomes, or three pairs, comprise the diploid complement of this hypothetical cell. Each chromosome duplicates its DNA during interphase and is seen as double in prophase. The double chromosomes separate at anaphase, and at telophase each daughter cell receives six chromosomes.

in detail here, but it might be well to note that this is the mechanism that determines that each daughter cell will obtain the same number and kind of chromosomes, and hence the same genes, as its parent cell. The cells of each kind of animal and plant have a characteristic chromosome number—forty-six for human cells, twenty-two in cells of the toad, eight for the fruit fly, twenty-eight in the tiger salamander, and so on. Organisms that begin their embryonic development with an abnormal number of chromosomes usually are defective and seldom survive.

If one arranges the metaphase chromosomes of a cell in order according to size and shape, he finds that they fall naturally into pairs. In the human being, for example, whereas there are forty-six chromosomes in each gonial cell (or each spleen cell, skin cell, and so on), there are only twenty-three different kinds, or pairs. We call the two chromosomes of each kind a *homologous pair;* if the number of homologous pairs is *n*, then the number of chromosomes in the cell is 2*n*. The *n* number of human chromosomes is twenty-three.

Because the new generation in sexually reproducing organisms is formed by the union of two cells, egg and sperm, it is evident that if each brought the $2n$ number of chromosomes to the union, the result-ing individual would have $4n$ chromosomes; in the next generation there would be offspring with $8n$ chromosomes, and so on. Quite evidently each gamete can contribute only one copy of each kind of chromosome at fertilization if the species-specific number of chromo-somes is to be maintained. Reduction of the chromosome number to n in the sexual cells is accomplished by the process called *meiosis;* and when sperm and egg unite, the $2n$ number is restored.

MEIOSIS

The nuclear changes that issue in the reduced number of chromo-somes are essentially the same in formation of the male and female gametes, but the associated phenomena that change the male cell into a sperm and the female cell into an egg, or ovum, are quite different. We shall first review briefly the basic nuclear changes (Figure 2·2) and then correlate these with the cytoplasmic modifications that lead to formation of the definitive gametes.

When the mitotic divisions of the spermatogonia and oögonia are finished, the first of two meiotic divisions begins. Each chromosome enters the prophase of the first meiotic division having already repli-cated, just as in the prophase of mitosis, so that it is actually made up of two *chromatids.* As the prophase condensation begins, each chromo-some comes to lie alongside its homologue (an event that does not occur in mitosis), so that there are formed the n number of pairs from the $2n$ number of chromosomes. But because each member of each pair comprises two chromatids, each of the pairs has a total of four chro-matids. This quadrapartite, or tetravalent, arrangement is called a *tetrad.* All four parts of the tetrad become readily visible during late prophase, when the chromosomes have coiled and contracted con-siderably. They now show rather bizarre shapes because of mechanical strains resulting from the exchange of pieces of chromatids between homologues—genetic *crossing over,* a very important aspect of inheri-tance in sexually reproducing organisms. Keep in mind that there are as many tetrads as there are kinds of chromosomes; that is, there is the n number. These can be counted rather easily at metaphase in many organisms.

During anaphase of the first meiotic division, the homologous chro-mosomes separate into *dyads,* bivalent structures, and each daughter cell receives as many dyads as there were tetrads before division, namely n.

In telophase, the daughter cells are promptly separated by the cell membrane, but a true interphase nucleus is seldom formed; the dyads move, instead, directly onto the metaphase spindle for a second meiotic

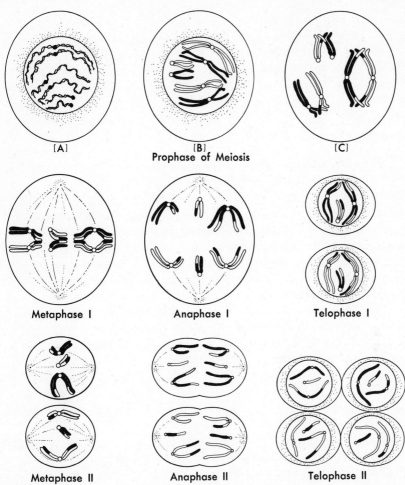

[A]

[B] Prophase of Meiosis

[C]

Metaphase I

Anaphase I

Telophase I

Metaphase II

Anaphase II

Telophase II

Figure 2·2. Meiosis: a summary of nuclear events in a hypothetical cell containing three pairs of chromosomes. Homologous chromosomes, already replicated, pair during early prophase and show the phenomenon known as crossing over. Tetrads are separated in two successive divisions, resulting in the formation of four cells, each with one representative of each kind of chromosome.

division. At the anaphase of the second division the dyads separate into *monads,* univalent daughter chromosomes, one going to each daughter cell. Thus the two divisions of meiosis result in the formation of four cells, each with the n number of chromosomes. (Recall that before the first division, the $2n$ number formed the n number of tetrads, and each tetrad was then separated into four parts by two successive divisions.)

The foregoing account is generally applicable to the nuclear changes that occur during the maturation of both sperm and eggs. The cytoplasmic events of gametogenesis are quite different for the germ cells of the two sexes, however, and each gamete brings an entirely different cytoplasmic endowment to the zygote. We shall first discuss *spermatogenesis,* formation of the sperm, and then *oögenesis,* formation of the ovum.

SPERMATOGENESIS

After the spermatogonia have ceased multiplication, they go through a relatively long period during which they grow slightly larger before beginning the early phases of meiotic prophase. At this stage they are *primary spermatocytes.* The primary spermatocyte shows the same sequence of chromosomal pairing and tetrad formation and division as described above for the first meiotic division. The daughter cells formed by this division are the *secondary spermatocytes.* These divide in the second meiotic division and, as the telophase is completed, the daughter nuclei take the form of the typical interphase nucleus, their chromosomes (*n* in number) appearing to lose their identity in a tangled mass of chromatin threads. The daughter cells are called *spermatids* at this stage. Four spermatids are formed by the divisions of the original primary spermatocyte, and each of these will transform into a spermatozoon.

This transformation is rather drastic for most kinds of spermatids (Figures 2·3 and 2·4), usually producing an elongate structure specialized for swimming and penetrating the ovum. During this transformation the nucleus loses fluid, shrinking to a compact, darkly staining mass; the cell becomes polarized, with the Golgi membrane system at one end and the mitochondria and centrioles at the other; the nucleus elongates; and a layer of closely packed microtubules, the *manchette,* arises and surrounds the nucleus in parallel array, oriented in the direction of the longitudinal axis of cell and nucleus. The Golgi apparatus produces the *acrosome,* a small body of importance for the interaction of egg and sperm, and an *acrosomal vesicle;* these adorn one end of the nucleus and, together with it, comprise the *head* of the spermatozoon. At the opposite end of the cell, one of the centrioles takes a position in an indentation of the nucleus and the other lies behind it. From the latter arises the axial filament of the *flagellum,* or *tail,* the propulsive organ of the sperm; the mitochondria, which provide the energy for propulsion, make an orderly spiral array around the axial filament at its proximal end, forming the *midpiece.* The bulk of the cytoplasm of the spermatid seems to flow away from the nuclear zone and is finally pinched off from the midpiece, leaving only a

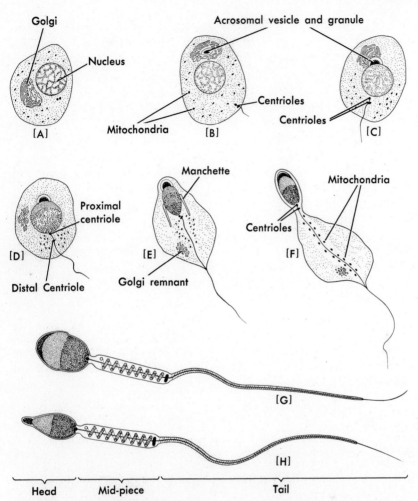

Figure 2·3. Transformation of the spermatid into spermatozoon. [Adapted, with modifications, from C. R. Austin, *Fertilization*, Englewood Cliffs, N.J.: Prentice-Hall, Inc., © 1965, p. 49. By permission.]

plasma membrane and thin sleeve of cytoplasm over nucleus and acrosome and extending around the midpiece and long tail.

Thus we see that basically the spermatozoon consists of a nucleus—the genetic endowment of the male parent—and the appropriate equipment for delivering itself to the egg, namely a power plant, a swimming organ, and an acrosome that aids in penetrating the egg cytoplasm. We shall see how delivery of the sperm nucleus is actually accomplished after reviewing what the ovum brings to the fertilization process.

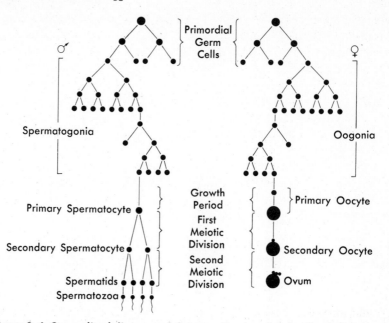

Figure 2·4. Generalized diagram of the germ line in animal cells. [Redrawn, with modifications, from E. B. Wilson, *The Cell*, 3d ed., New York: Macmillan, 1928, p. 311.]

OÖGENESIS

Usually the ovum is much larger than the sperm. Whereas sperm have dimensions of only a few microns (except for the length of the slender tail) and are visible only with the aid of the microscope, most eggs are tens or hundreds of microns in diameter and may measure several centimeters across, as do, for example, the eggs of many birds. Eggs are nonmotile, as a rule, and their larger size results from the presence of quantities of energy-rich material, yolk, which is accumulated while they are in the ovary and before meiosis occurs.

When the oögonial divisions are finished, the egg becomes a *primary oöcyte* and then embarks on what may be a relatively prolonged period of growth, during which its size may increase many times. It reaches its final size before the meiotic divisions take place. Both the nucleus and cytoplasm participate in this enlargement during the growth phase. In the enlarging oöcyte nucleus, the chromatin material may become so diluted as to be almost undetectable. In this enlarged state the oöcyte nucleus is referred to as the *germinal vesicle.* Yolk, which accumulates in the cytoplasm, is not a chemical entity but a mixture of things, mostly proteins—such as phosphovitellin and lipovitellin—and phospholipids and neutral fats. In some eggs, the yolk is apparently synthesized entirely within the oöcyte: in crayfish, a good deal of this synthesis goes on in an elaborate ribosome-studded endo-plasmic reticulum; in amphibians, yolk platelets have been described as crystallizing within the mitochrondria. In insects, it has been shown that proteins injected into the blood may be picked up directly by the oöcytes and incorporated into the yolk.

Eggs of various organisms differ considerably in the amount of yolk they contain, in the way it is distributed, and in the time of its utilization. The eggs of many marine invertebrates have very little yolk and develop within a short time after fertilization into larval forms that, although composed of only a few cells, are capable of swimming and feeding. Obviously, such eggs need but little stored energy for this limited development. After a period of feeding, the larvae are ready to transform into the adult configuration. Other marine eggs have considerable yolk, and many of them bypass the larval stages, using their energy supply to develop quickly to the feeding-adult state.

The egg of the mammal has very little yolk. Unlike marine eggs similarly endowed, it does not develop quickly to an independent form; instead, it rapidly develops structures that enable it to relate to maternal tissues and to receive an energy supply from the blood stream of the mother (see Chapter 3). In other organisms, the egg has an abundant yolk, which is not used up during embryonic life. The tadpole of the frog, for example, retains in the cells of its alimentary tract large quantities of yolk that are used for continued growth and differentiation after hatching. Some newly hatched fish actually swim about with a yolk sac attached to the belly. For aquatic vertebrates such as these, there is probably a considerable survival advantage in a period of rapid development that leaves a free-swimming larval form able to escape readily from the egg clutch and swim about with its own energy supply.

DISTRIBUTION OF YOLK. In eggs of most animals, the yolk is not distributed evenly throughout the cytoplasm (Figure 2·5B). Usually at one end of the egg there is an area that is relatively free of yolk. The nucleus lies in this region, and it is here that the mitotic spindles appear and the polar bodies (daughter nuclei of meiosis that are discarded) are formed. This region is referred to as the *animal pole*.

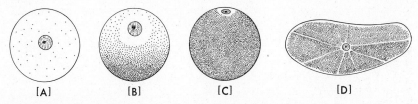

[A]　　　[B]　　　[C]　　　[D]

Figure 2·5. The distribution of yolk in isolecithal (**A**), telolecithal (**B** and **C**), and centrolecithal (**D**) eggs.

Directly opposite the animal pole is the *vegetal pole,* where the concentration of yolk is greatest. The *animal-vegetal axis* is characterized by a gradient in yolk concentration, the concentration increasing from animal pole to vegetal pole in most kinds of eggs.

Some eggs have very little yolk and there is little or no gradient in its distribution along the animal-vegetal axis (Figure 2·5A). These eggs are called *isolecithal* (little yolk), and the egg of man is an example. Even though a yolk gradient may not be detected, the position of the animal pole may be determined as the point where the meiotic divisions take place and the polar bodies are formed.

Eggs that have a noticeably greater concentration of yolk at the vegetal pole are called *telolecithal* (yolk at one end). Most amphibians have eggs in which there is a very strong yolk gradient, the region of the animal pole showing small and scattered yolk platelets that grade progressively into the larger yolk masses occupying the vegetal pole, almost to the exclusion of the cytoplasm (Figure 2·5B). Eggs of birds present extreme cases in this category of egg types. The great bulk of the bird's egg consists of yolk, with only a thin disk of nucleated protoplasm at the animal pole (Figure 2·5C). In fish eggs, which are somewhat similar, some cytoplasm is present throughout the yolk zone before fertilization, especially peripherally, but most of this flows into a protoplasmic disk at the animal pole after fertilization.

Eggs of many arthropods and some coelenterates are described as *centrolecithal.* They are relatively large, are usually elongate, and have a very great amount of yolk (Figure 2·5D). The nucleus lies near the geometric center of the yolk mass, surrounded by a small amount of cytoplasm. A thin cytoplasmic layer covers the surface of the yolk and sends fine strands into the zone occupied by the nucleus.

MEMBRANES.   A special feature of the development of the ovum is its acquisition of protective membranes. In addition to the plasma membrane, there is almost always a *vitelline membrane,* which is formed during the growth and differentiation of the ovum, usually through its cooperation with the surrounding cells. Plasma membrane and vitelline membrane are referred to as *primary egg membranes.* Other membranes may be added as the egg passes through the oviduct before or after fertilization. These are called *secondary egg membranes.* Examples are the shell membranes and shell of the hen's egg and the jelly membranes of the frog egg (Figure 2·6).

MATURATION OF THE OVUM.   The meiotic divisions may occur before the egg leaves the ovary or not until considerably later. But regardless of where or when they occur, the result of the meiotic divisions is not four fertilizable eggs, but only one (Figure 2·4). At the onset of the first meiotic division in the primary oöcyte, the chromosomes form tetrads, as they do in formation of the male gamete; in the

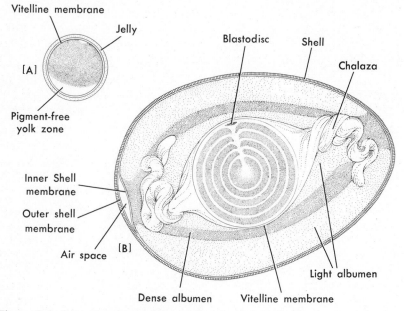

Figure 2·6. Primary and secondary membranes of the unfertilized egg of the frog (A) and the egg of the hen (B).

oöcyte, however, the spindle on which the tetrads are arranged is quite small as compared with the total volume of the cell. It moves to the periphery of the egg at the animal pole, a site relatively free from yolk, and as separation of the dyad chromosomes takes place at anaphase, a small blob of cytoplasm pinches off, taking away one daughter nucleus and leaving the other inside the egg. The one outside is the *first polar body*. The polar body and egg nucleus now each contain as many dyads as there were tetrads during anaphase; that is, they each have the *n* number. The egg is now a *secondary oöcyte*. Although nuclei of polar body and oöcyte are essentially the same, only that of the egg will contribute anything to the next generation. The polar body may divide again during the second meiotic division or it may not; eventually it degenerates.

As soon as the first polar body is extruded, the dyads remaining within the egg form at the metaphase plate of a new spindle ready for the second meiotic division. This division likewise pinches off a nucleus outside the main body of the egg, the *second polar body*. It, like the first, degenerates. The daughter nucleus remaining within the egg now contains the *n* number of monads: it quickly re-forms the nuclear membrane; the chromosomes lose their compact appearance and their morphological distinctness. It is now the *female pronucleus*, and the egg cell is an *oötid*, or ovum.

By analogy with what we have seen in the differentiation of the sperm, we would expect that for the ovum the completion of the events of meiosis would be requisite for readiness for fertilization. Actually, the time at which the egg is ready for fertilization, or ripe, is quite variable with respect to the time at which meiosis takes place. In some animals, meiosis has not yet begun at the time the egg is fertilized. Indeed, if fertilization does not occur in these forms, the meiotic divisions do not ensue, and the egg becomes unfertilizable after a time and dies. In other animals meiosis proceeds to the first or to the second meiotic metaphase before fertilization can occur. In man and in most vertebrate animals, the egg is not ripe until the metaphase of the second meiotic division, meiosis proceeding only if fertilization takes place. In many of the invertebrate animals, eggs are not ready for fertilization until after meiosis is complete.

Fertilization

The morphological events of fertilization may be listed under three principal headings: (1) activation of the sperm, (2) cortical reaction of the egg, and (3) union of male and female pronuclei and combination of the hereditary material from the two parents. These events

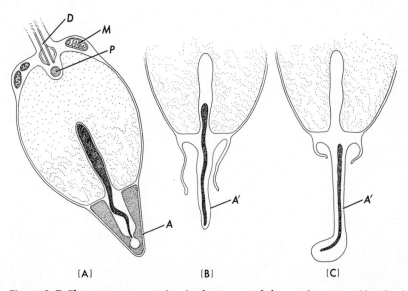

[A]   [B]   [C]

Figure 2·7. The acrosome reaction in the sperm of the marine worm Nereis. A: The head of the unreacted spermatozoon. **B** and **C:** Successive stages of the acrosome reaction. A, acrosome; A', acrosomal filament; D, distal centriole; M, mitochondrion; N, nucleus; P, proximole centriole; R, rodlike core of acrosomal filament. [Redrawn from material supplied by Dr. John F. Fallon and Dr. C. R. Austin. C. R. Austin, *Fertilization*, © 1965. By permission of Prentice-Hall, Inc., Englewood Cliffs, New Jersey.]

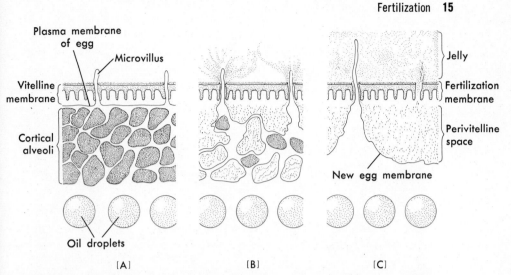

Figure 2·8. The fertilization reaction in the cortex of the egg of Nereis, showing fusion and rupture of the cortical alveoli, formation of a new cytoplasmic surface, the release of jelly precursor, and its passage through the vitelline membrane. **A:** Unreacted egg cortex. **B:** Ten minutes after fertilization. **C:** Twenty minutes after fertilization. [Redrawn from original drawings supplied by Dr. John F. Fallon and Dr. C. R. Austin.]

have been studied most intensively in eggs of marine invertebrates whose gametes are normally shed directly into the sea water.

When the gametes are mixed, the first reaction is shown by the sperm; its acrosome discharges the contents of the acrosomal vesicle and forms a tubule that elongates rapidly, in some cases projecting far beyond the sperm head (Figure 2·7). For the successful sperm, the tip of the acrosomal tubule makes contact with the surface of the egg through the vitelline membrane, the penetration possibly being aided by the action of lytic enzymes released from the acrosomal vesicle.

Contact by the sperm evokes a dramatic reaction in that part of the egg immediately below the vitelline membrane (Figure 2·8), which is called the *cortex*. It contains, in most species, rather prominent and closely spaced *cortical alveoli;* they are usually less than a micron in diameter and contain sulfonated glycoproteins. At the point on the egg where the sperm makes contact, the cortical alveoli begin to rupture in a wave that spreads rapidly in all directions around the egg to the opposite side. The discharge of their contents beneath the vitelline membrane effectively destroys the egg-cell membrane and creates a fluid-filled space. A new limiting membrane for the egg, now somewhat shrunken, is formed at the inner limits of this zone, possibly incorporating fragments of the membranes that once surrounded the cortical alveoli. The space between the new egg membrane and the old vitelline membrane is called the *perivitelline space,* and the vitelline membrane is now called the *fertilization membrane.*

The perivitelline space begins to appear first at the point of sperm contact, where in some eggs, the surface of the egg protrudes toward the sperm in the form of a *fertilization cone* that intrudes into the perivitelline space (Figure 2·9). The covering membrane of the egg

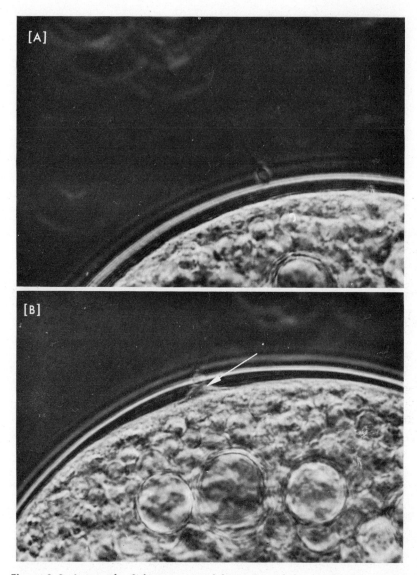

Figure 2·9. Approach of the sperm and formation of the fertilization cone in Nereis. In **A** the head of the sperm has made contact with the vitelline membrane. In **B**, twelve minutes later, the egg has elevated a fertilization cone (arrow) which is beginning to engulf the sperm. [Photographs supplied by Dr. John F. Fallon.]

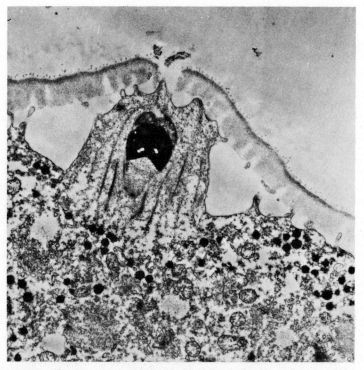

Figure 2·10. Electron micrograph of the sperm head of the marine worm *Urechis caupo* within the fertilization cone formed by the egg cortex, five minutes after fertilization. [From A. Tyler, in *Am. Naturalist*, 99:309–344, 1965. By courtesy of Dr. Tyler and permission of *The American Naturalist*.]

at the tip of the fertilization cone become confluent with the limiting membrane of the acrosomal tubule, and because the latter is continuous with the plasma membrane of the sperm, both egg and sperm now share a continuous membrane. The distance progressively shortens between sperm and egg, and the naked sperm nucleus is gradually drawn into the interior of the egg (Figure 2·10).

When fertilization is accomplished, in nature or in the laboratory, there are myriads of sperm surrounding every egg, and yet only one sperm normally penetrates the membranes surrounding the egg (monospermy). It has been suggested that the elevation of the fertilization membrane constitutes a block to polyspermy, i.e., to entrance of additional sperm; but in some cases removal of the fertilization membrane permits more sperm to enter the egg, and in other cases it does not. It is not really known what constitutes the block to polyspermy in nature, but a block does seem to be established very quickly, spreading over the surface of the egg from the point of contact of the first sperm and proceeding much more rapidly than the formation of the fertilization membrane. Some eggs are unusual in that they regularly permit several sperm to enter; but in such cases only one sperm survives to contribute the genetic material of the male parent, the others disintegrating. Sometimes overripe eggs, i.e., eggs that have aged beyond the normal time for fertilization, permit the entry of several sperm. This is an abnormal condition and usually leads to pathological development.

After the sperm has entered the egg, it may remain quiescent until the egg has completed its meiotic divisions if these are incomplete. Thereafter, it acquires a nuclear membrane, possibly contributed by the cytoplasm of the egg and is then called the *male pronucleus*. With meiotic divisions completed, the egg nucleus becomes the female pronucleus. The two pronuclei move toward each other and lie side by side as the mitotic spindle for the first cell division forms (see cover illustration).

Sorting the Materials of the Egg: Formation of Germ Layers

CELL DIVISION ALONE is not a sufficient mechanism to effect the transformation of the fertilized egg into a functioning organism. The events that take place during this transformation are complex, but the problem of understanding them may be simplified if we reduce to simple form what it is that the organism accomplishes in development. One way of doing this is to schematize the body plan of the animal to be formed and then to determine, if possible, whence each part of the plan takes its origin.

First we can recognize that each organism has a part of its body through which it makes contact with the external environment. For simplicity, let us call that part of the body the *outer layer* and schematize it this way:

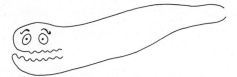

The outer layer comprises the skin, central nervous system, and sense organs. It is the covering of the animal, the part that communicates directly to the exterior and that senses the external environment and mediates the reactions of the organism to it.

In the basic body plan we recognize another part whose function it is to receive the incoming food and to process it mechanically and chemically so that its high-energy compounds and protoplasmic building blocks are available to the cellular machinery throughout the organism. These functions are carried out by a part of the animal that we shall call the *inner layer*. It may be diagramed this way:

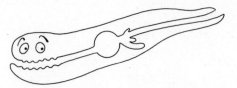

We recognize the inner layer as the alimentary tract—esophagus, stomach, liver, pancreas, small and large intestines, and so on. It is essentially a tube that connects anterior and posterior openings of the outer layer.

The final aspect of the plan must represent the parts that nourish, support, and move the structures formed by the outer and inner layers. These parts are the vascular system, bone, cartilage, tendon, skeletal and smooth muscle, and so on; they comprise what we shall call the *middle layer*. The relationship of the middle to the other layers may be illustrated by filling in the spaces between the inner and outer layers:

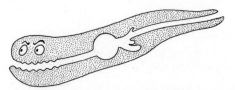

We have now simplified the task of understanding what the egg must do—it must make three layers of tissue and arrange them into inner, middle, and outer regions. It does this according to a construction plan that can be represented with great simplicity, if we forget details for a moment. First, by mitotic cell division the fertilized egg becomes many cells. These then arrange themselves in a fluid-filled ball that may be represented this way:

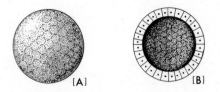

[A]   [B]

If we regard the walls of this ball as a layer, then we have at this time a one-layered animal.

By a relatively simple (simple to draw, at any rate) maneuver, the ball becomes two-layered. Imagine that you push in the wall of a dead tennis ball with your index finger—imagine you do the same to a fluid-filled ball of cells. What happens? The one-layered structure transforms into a two-layered one:

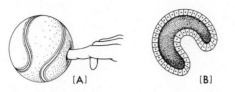

[A]   [B]

There are several ways in which the three-layered form can arise from the two-layered configuration, but the simplest case to illustrate is the one in which some of the cells at the junction of inner and outer layers escape from their neighbors and invade the space between the first two layers:

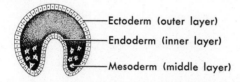

Ectoderm (outer layer)
Endoderm (inner layer)
Mesoderm (middle layer)

The three layers thereby formed are collectively termed *germ layers*. They have been given names derived from Greek roots that can be translated into terms similar to those we have already applied to them. The outer layer is *ectoderm* (*ekto* means outside and *derma* means skin); the inner layer is *endoderm* (*endos* means within); the middle layer is *mesoderm* (*meso* means middle). We speak of the skin, sense organs, and nervous system as arising from ectoderm; of the muscles, blood, and bone as mesodermal derivatives; and of the alimentary tract as originating from endoderm.

The foregoing should suggest that understanding the sequence of morphological changes that take place in development is not an impossible task—in outline at least. To start to apply the basic plan of development to finite cases, we shall examine the development of representatives from different groups of organisms to find how they achieve first the multicellular condition and then the three-layered condition. The mechanical changes they all undergo are summed up in two terms: *cleavage* and *gastrulation*. The significance of these terms will become more meaningful as we proceed.

Cleavage and Gastrulation

The term *cleavage* is applied to the first few cell divisions of the fertilized egg. The end of the cleavage period comes, in the simplest cases, when the cells formed by division have arranged themselves about a central cavity. The embryo is then called a *blastula,* and the cavity is the *blastocoele.* The blastula undergoes mechanical changes that lead to the three-layered condition; during this process, which is called *gastrulation,* it is referred to as a *gastrula.*

The various ways in which protoplasm and yolk are arranged in eggs of different kinds determine that the processes of cleavage and gastrulation will necessarily differ from one kind of egg to another. Such differences notwithstanding, the basic plan of cleavage and gastrulation may be learned from certain forms that show the processes in relatively uncomplicated fashion; the developmental patterns of other forms can then be analyzed as variations of a basic pattern.

SEA URCHINS

Sea urchins are echinoderms—relatives of starfish, sea cucumbers, and brittle stars. Numerous species of sea urchins are found in coastal waters throughout the world, from just below the tidal zone down to considerable depths. Their eggs are favorite objects of embryological study, for they can be obtained in great numbers from one species or another during most of the year and the plan of cleavage and gastrulation shown by many of them is particularly suitable for the experimental analysis of cell division and morphogenetic movements.

Most sea-urchin eggs have very little yolk, and the cleavages divide the protoplasm completely. After union of the pronuclei, the first mitotic spindle forms at right angles to the animal-vegetal axis. During telophase the egg is divided into two daughter cells of equal size by means of a furrow that passes directly through the animal and vegetal poles. We say that this first cleavage furrow is *meridional* (Figure 3·1A,B).

The daughter cells lie side by side, somewhat flattened against each other. Soon their nuclei prepare for the second cleavage division; the mitotic spindles form anew, again with their axes at right angles to the animal-vegetal axis of the egg. In this division, however, their axes are also at right angles to the axis of the first cleavage spindle. Cleavage furrows appear simultaneously in each cell and pass through the animal and vegetal poles at right angles to the first division furrow (Figure 3·1B,C). Two successive meridional divisions thus produce four *blastomeres,* the term applied to all cells produced during cleavage.

The four blastomeres now divide, but this time the mitotic spindles are aligned parallel to the animal-vegetal axis and, simultaneously in each cell, a *latitudinal* cleavage furrow appears just above the equator of the egg. There are now eight blastomeres, upper and lower tiers of four each, with the lower tier usually composed of cells slightly larger than those in the upper (Figure 3·1D).

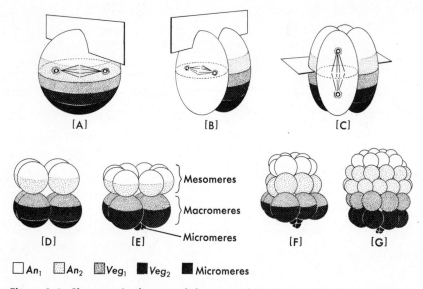

$\square$ An₁ $\square$ An₂ $\blacksquare$ Veg₁ $\blacksquare$ Veg₂ $\blacksquare$ Micromeres

Figure 3·1. Cleavage in the egg of the sea urchin. A, B, and **C** show positions of the cleavage spindles in the one-, two-, and four-cell stages, respectively. **D, E, F,** and **G:** eight,- sixteen-, thirty-two-, and sixty-four-cell stages resulting from the third, fourth, fifth, and sixth cleavages, respectively. [Adapted from C. H. Waddington, *Principles of Embryology*, New York: Macmillan, 1956, p. 80.]

In eggs of many marine organisms, this stage is followed by simultaneous cleavages that are alternately meridional and latitudinal, so that the embryo comprises sixteen, then thirty-two, then sixty-four, then one hundred twenty-eight cells, and so on, the cells gradually arranging themselves around a central cavity as they continue to divide. In the sea urchin, however, this pattern is not followed (Figure 3·1D). At the fourth cleavage the upper tier of cells divides meridionally to form a ring of eight cells, but in the lower tier, the spindles arrange themselves obliquely so that four small cells are pinched off from the lower inner sides of the larger cells. The small cells are called *micromeres,* and those whence they came are *macromeres.* The cells of the upper tier, intermediate in size, are called *mesomeres* (Figure 3·1E).

Subsequent cleavages proceed more or less synchronously for some time in all cells. As the thirty-two-cell stage is formed, the eight mesomeres are cut by horizontal furrows to give two rings of eight cells each, an_1 and an_2, one above the other; the four macromeres are cut meridionally, however, so they form a ring of eight cells below an_2 (Figure 3·1F). At the sixth cleavage all division planes are horizontal, so there are formed two rings of eight cells each in an_1 and two rings of daughter cells from each of the macromeres—the upper one veg_1, the lower one veg_2. At the vegetal pole, by this time, are sixteen micro-

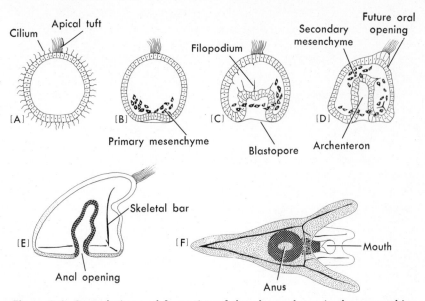

Figure 3·2. Gastrulation and formation of the pluteus larva in the sea urchin.
A: Blastula. B: Mesenchyme blastula. C: Invagination of the endoderm. D: Continued
invagination and formation of secondary mesenchyme. E: Prism larva viewed from
the right. F: Pluteus viewed from the aboral side. [B, C, and D adapted from J. P.
Trinkaus, after T. Gustafson and L. Wolpert, in R. L. DeHaan and H. Ursprung (eds.),
Organogenesis, New York: Holt, 1965, p. 86. E and F adapted from C. H. Waddington, *Principles of Embryology*, New York: Macmillan, 1956, p. 80.]

meres (Figure 3·1G). In the next division, a meridional one, the
stage of one hundred twenty-eight cells is reached. By this time the cells
are arranged in the typical configuration of the blastula, that is, about
a fluid-filled center (Figure 3·2A). They continue to multiply as
development proceeds.

CONCEPT OF PROSPECTIVE FATE. The outer cells of the blastula
develop cilia that whip rhythmically, causing the blastula to rotate
within its fertilization membrane, whence it soon breaks out. At the
animal pole, the cilia become longer and coarser, forming an *apical
tuft*. Soon thereafter, the blastula loses its spherical shape, becoming
flattened at the end opposite the apical tuft, i.e., at the vegetal pole.
This is the first sign of gastrulation (Figure 3·2B). Cells begin to move
singly from the center of this flattened zone into the blastocoele. These
are mesoderm cells, and they are referred to as the *primary mesenchyme*. About the same time, the entire vegetal region turns inward,
pushing toward the animal pole and creating a new cavity, the *primitive gut*, or *archenteron*, whose cells comprise the endoderm. As the
gut wall pushes toward the animal pole, cells wander out from it,
forming additional mesodermal cells, the *secondary mesenchyme* (Fig-

ure 3·2C,D). The opening of the archenteron to the outside is the *blastopore*. Gastrulation is thus accomplished in the sea urchin by relatively simple component processes: the *ingression* of mesodermal cells from the original vegetal pole and the *invagination*, or inward folding, of the endoderm, the ectoderm being left as the outer covering. The simplicity with which these processes are described is deceptive, for the analysis of their component ordering forces has thus far enjoyed only uncertain success.

The gastrula transforms quickly into a prism-shaped larva, then into a more definitive stage called a *pluteus* (Figure 3·2E,F), and it remains in the latter condition as a feeding organism before undergoing metamorphosis to the adult form. Embryonic development is essentially complete with the formation of the pluteus, and it is of interest now to note that the origin of is various parts can be traced back to definite regions of the blastula or even earlier stages. Thus the descendants of the micromeres, formed during the fourth cleavage, are the cells whence arise the mesoderm. It is the *prospective fate* of these cells to give rise to the skeletal bars of the pluteus. The cells of veg_2, separated from veg_1 at the sixth cleavage, are those that invaginate at gastrulation. It is their prospective fate to form the gut and secondary mesenchyme. The prospective fate of the remaining cells, those of an_1, an_2, and veg_1, is to form the ectoderm, the outer covering of the pluteus.

ANNELIDS AND MOLLUSKS

The eggs of a great many marine annelids and mollusks (flatworms and nemerteans, too) show a variation of the basic cleavage pattern that is called *spiral*. A useful organism in which to study spiral cleavage is the shoreline dweller *Crepidula,* a mollusk in which each blastomere formed during cleavage can be recognized by its position and size and followed to its ultimate developmental fate. One of the first cell-lineage studies was carried out on *Crepidula* by E. G. Conklin at the turn of this century, and his system for identifying each blastomere is still used in embryological studies of spirally cleaving eggs.

The first two cleavages are meridional and produce four large blastomeres called macromeres, designated arbitrarily as *A, B, C,* and *D* (Figure 3·3A–D). In subsequent cleavages, each macromere pinches off a small cell, a micromere, at the animal pole, and each successive quartet of micromeres is displaced alternately to the right or left of its macromere of origin, as the upper ends of the mitotic spindles for each cleavage shift alternately clockwise and counterclockwise (as seen from the animal pole). We say that the cleavages spiral alternately to the left and right (Figure 3·3E,F). The cleavage divisions leave the

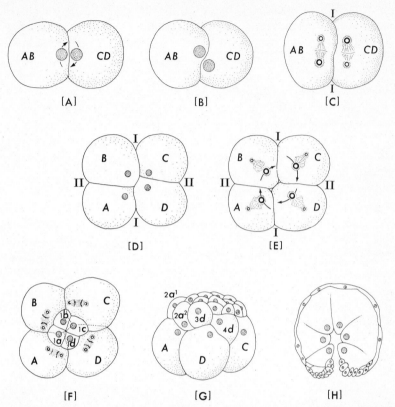

Figure 3·3. Cleavage and gastrulation in *Crepidula*. A to **F:** Views from the animal pole. **G** and **H:** Views from the side. The first meridional division is completed in **A**, and the first cleavage furrow bends to the right in **B**. In **C**, the anaphase spindles form with their left ends (in the counterclockwise sense) higher toward the animal pole than their right ends, so that cells A and C are cut off in **D** at a higher level of focus than B and D. In **E**, the spindles for the third cleavage form with their upper ends closer to the animal-vegetal axis than their lower ends; the upper ends swing to the right (arrows), and in **F** small daughter cells, micromeres, are cut off to the right of the lower macromeres. The twenty-nine—cell stage is shown in **G**, and a section through the animal-vegetal axis of the gastrula is shown in **H**. [Adapted from E. G. Conklin, in *J. Morphol.*, 13:1–226, 1897.]

macromeres with a cap of micromeres at the animal pole (Figure 3·3G). This configuration is what constitutes the blastula in spirally cleaving forms, there being no blastocoele.

Gastrulation is accomplished through the overgrowth of the macromeres by the micromeres and the shifting of the latter to accommodate a small archenteron (Figure 3·3H). The macromeres comprise the prospective endoderm, and the micromeres contribute the ectodermal derivatives for the most part. In many forms with spiral cleavage, during the sixth division the *D* macromere produces its fourth daughter cell, $4d$, precociously. This cell, budded off beneath overlying micromeres, is the ancestral cell of the mesoderm.

FROGS AND URODELES

The eggs of amphibians are large and easily seen within their jelly coats by the unaided eye. There is a darkly pigmented zone at the center of which is the animal pole and a relatively unpigmented region, comprising large yolk masses, at the vegetal pole. The eggs of frogs and urodeles are very much alike, and the description that follows applies, for the most part, to the development of both.

When freshly shed, the eggs are clamped tightly within their jelly membranes (Figure 2·6A); but upon fertilization, the vitelline membrane is lifted off as a kind of fertilization membrane, and the egg soon becomes free to rotate within the perivitelline space. This it does, with its heavier, yolk-laden vegetal pole taking the lower position and the pigmented animal pole taking the upper. One may then watch with the dissecting microscope the formation of the second polar body at the animal pole.

After fertilization it can be observed (with varying ease from one batch of eggs to the next) that on one side of the egg the pigment at the junction of the dark and lighter zones shifts upward, diluting the dark color to gray in a crescent-shaped zone appropriately called the *gray crescent* (Figure 3·4A,B). It probably forms in the region of the junction that was uppermost when the egg rotated within its membranes. The eccentric position of the gray crescent in the egg cortex determines that only one plane divides the egg into mirror-twin halves. The egg is thus bilaterally symmetrical prior to its first cleavage.

The first cleavage in the frog is meridional and usually bisects the gray crescent, thus dividing the germ along the plane of symmetry. The next cleavage is also meridional and, in the usual pattern, takes place at right angles to the first. This results in an embryo of four cells, two of which contain material of the gray crescent (Figure 3·4C,D). We shall consider the significance of this distribution of the gray crescent later.

The first two cleavage furrows appear initially at the animal pole, cutting swiftly through the protoplasm in that region; then proceeding more slowly, they enter the yolk-laden vegetal region. At the four-cell stage, the mitotic spindles for the next division form considerably above the equator of the egg, and the third cleavage, which is horizontal, cuts off four small cells at the animal pole and four large, yolk-filled cells below (Figure 3·4E). The next cleavage is a meridional one and is completed much more rapidly in cells of the animal half of the egg than in the yolky vegetal-pole cells (Figure 3·4F). Division continues

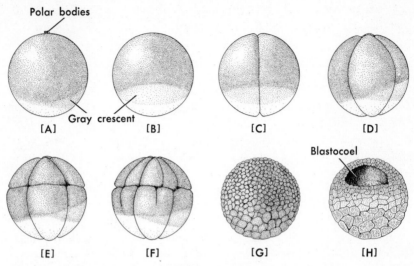

Figure 3·4. Cleavage of the amphibian egg. The uncleaved zygote is seen from the left side in **A** and from the future posterior side in **B.** In **C,** the first cleavage is shown to bisect the gray crescent. **D:** Four-cell stage. **E:** Eight cells. **F:** Sixteen cells. The early blastula is shown in exterior view in **G** and with one side cut away in **H.**

rapidly in the cells of the pigmented half, cutting the protoplasm into ever smaller cells, for no growth occurs between cleavages. By the time several hundred cells have been formed, they have arranged themselves about a small, eccentrically placed, fluid-filled cavity. The embryo is now a blastula, and the cavity is the blastocoele, according to the usual terminology (Figure 3·4G,H).

The blastocoele is nearer the animal pole, and its roof is formed of layers of small cells that rapidly become increasingly smaller as cell division proceeds. The floor of the cavity, however, comprises a thick layer of large yolky cells that divide slowly. It might be expected that these cells, like the macromeres of *Crepidula,* would not be able to form endoderm by invagination from the vegetal pole, as occurs in the sea urchin. This seems to be so, and the amphibian has evolved its peculiar pattern of gastrular movements. We shall examine these movements but first must view their consequences in order to understand better what they are accomplishing.

Figure 3·5 illustrates the structure of a frog embryo in the *neurula* stage, which is formed soon after gastrulation is completed. The ectoderm forms on the dorsal side a plate of cells that rolls up and develops into the brain and spinal cord; it is called the *neural plate.* A segregation of mesodermal cells in the dorsal midline forms the *notochord,* a supporting rod that runs the length of the embryo. Adjacent to the notochord on each side, the mesoderm becomes arranged into a band of tissue, the *segmental plate*. It is continuous with the *lateral plate* of the mesoderm, which extends as a sheet beneath the ectoderm and surrounds the inner mass. The segmental plate later forms most of the skeleton and musculature of the back. The lateral plate splits into *splanchnic* and *somatic layers,* the latter forming the appendages and body wall, the former investing the visceral organs. The inner mass of yolk-filled cells comprises, of course, the endoderm, which forms the lining of the alimentary tract and gives rise to the major digestive glands.

In order to learn how this arrangement of parts is achieved from the relatively simple structure of the blastula, one may mark spots on the surface of the blastula by applying to it small bits of agar stained with harmless dyes. The cells in contact with the agar will pick up the dye, retaining it throughout gastrulation; dissection of the embryo at the gastrula or later stages enables the disposition of the marked cells to be determined. By systematically marking parts of the blastula, one may determine their prospective fates and construct *fate maps.* Such a map for the blastula of a urodele is shown in Figure 3·6. Note that the prospective ectodermal organs—skin and nervous system—occupy most of the animal half of the egg; the prospective mesodermal derivatives are below them, and the yolky cells of the future endoderm are entirely in the vegetal half. The disposition of notochord and other mesodermal zones shows clearly that the materials of the embryo are arranged in a pattern of bilateral symmetry, the plane of symmetry passing through both poles and through the center of the notochordal material.

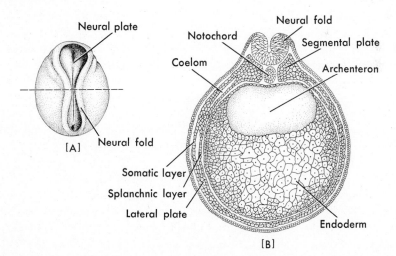

Figure 3·5. The neurula of the amphibian. A: Dorsal view. B: Cross section.

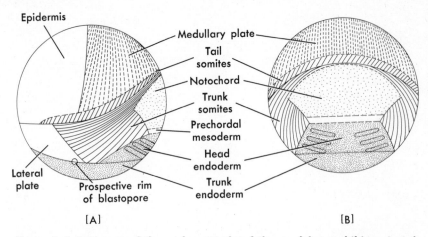

Figure 3·6. Fate map of the early gastrula of the urodele amphibian. A: Left side. **B:** Posterior view. [Adapted from J. Pasteels, in *J. Exp. Zool.*, 89:255–282, 1942, fig. 12a and 12b.]

It is evident that for the future ectodermal cells to envelop the endodermal yolk mass and for the meosdermal cells to become inserted as a middle layer between them, the gastrulation process must involve dramatic movements of cells. These movements are complex, but may be resolved into three principal components: *ingression,* or inward shifting of yolky cells from the vegetal region; *epiboly,* the covering over of the vegetal half by cells of the animal half; and *invagination* of cells through the blastopore.

In urodeles, the first external sign of gastrulation is the appearance of a tiny crescentic groove at the marginal zone where the gray crescent meets the yellow yolk, just below the region of the prospective notochord (Figure 3·7A). This groove is formed by the ingression of the yolky cells whose fate it is to form the endoderm of the head region. As gastrulation proceeds, the groove deepens and gradually spreads around the marginal zone, first as a half-moon and finally as a full circle. The circle is the blastopore, and the site of the first ingression is referred to as the *dorsal lip of the blastopore.*

As the groove deepens dorsally, the future notochordal material stretches out, converges on the dorsal lip, and wheels around the rim of the blastopore to invaginate as a cell sheet. With the spreading of the blastopore laterally and ventrally, the invagination progressively involves mesoderm of the trunk and tail somites and the lateral plate. Meanwhile, the remaining external surface area continues to expand, so that the entire yolk mass gradually becomes enveloped by it. The progress of invagination may be followed in Figure 3·7, where both the external and internal changes are illustrated. Invagination through the blastopore forms the cavity of the archenteron and gradually obliterates the old blastopore. The roof of the archenteron is formed of mesoderm, which, in the midline, constitutes the material of the notochord; laterally, it comprises the future somites and lateral plate.

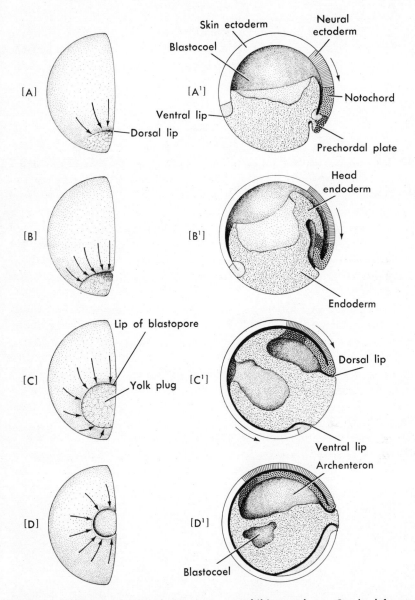

Figure 3·7. Stages of gastrulation in an amphibian embryo. On the left, cutaway left halves are shown in surface view from the future posterodorsal angle. On the right, the internal changes are shown in the corresponding right halves viewed from the left side. [A′–D′ adapted from O. E. Nelsen, *Comparative Embryology of the Vertebrates*, New York: McGraw-Hill, 1953, p. 409.]

The floor of the archenteron consists of yolk-filled endodermal cells. Toward the end of gastrulation, endodermal cells rise up the sides of the archenteron and close over dorsally to isolate the lumen of future gut.

Gastrulation follows a similar pattern in the frog, the chief difference lying in the fact that the blastopore arises entirely within the endodermal zone instead of at its margin. This causes the roof of the archenteron to be lined with endoderm from the beginning of gastrulation.

BIRDS

The earliest stages of development in birds are difficult to study, for they occur before the egg is laid. The egg, a tiny disk of nucleated protoplasm atop a great mass of yolk, is released from the ovary and fertilized by sperm previously stored in special folds of the mucosal lining of the oviduct. As the egg travels down the oviduct, it acquires its secondary coverings—albumin coat, shell membranes, and shell (Figure 2·5). Meanwhile cleavage occurs, the protoplasmic disk, but not the yolk, dividing repeatedly (Figure 3·8) until there are about sixty thousand cells (estimated for the chick) arranged as a sheet, the *blastoderm,* atop the yolk.

Gastrulation in birds is only now becoming understood and many details remain to be analyzed. The cells of the freshly laid egg of the chicken are usually arranged in two layers, an upper one called the *epiblast* and a lower one called the *hypoblast.* Earlier, however, they comprised a single layer several cells in thickness. From this layer cells detached themselves, singly and in clusters, to form the hypoblast; the latter is separated by a cleft from the overlying epiblast, now a single layer of cells (Figure 3·9).

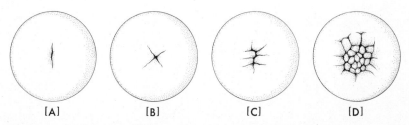

[A]   [B]   [C]   [D]

Figure 3·8. Cleavage of the bird's egg in surface view. Early cleavages are in planes perpendicular to the surface of the yolk, forming a single layer of cells. The blastoderm becomes multilayered later as a consequence of cell divisions in planes tangential to the surface. [Interpretative drawings; based on photographs of living and fixed eggs of the hen, by M. W. Olsen, in *J. Morphol.* 70:513–533, 1942, and of the pigeon, by M. Blount, in *Biol. Bull.,* 13:231–250, 1907.]

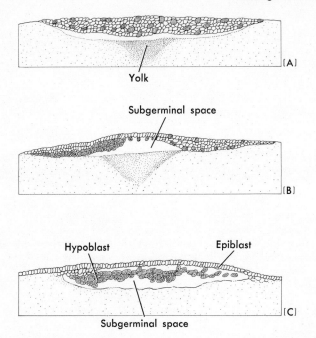

Figure 3·9. Sagittal sections through the blastoderm of the egg of the duck at successive stages, depicting the subsurface segregation of cells to form the hypoblast. [Adapted from T. W. Torrey, in *Morphogenesis of the Vertebrates,* New York: Wiley, 1962, p. 120.]

Centrally, the blastoderm of the newly laid egg comprises cells relatively free of yolk overlying a fluid-filled *subgerminal space.* Marginally, the cells are laden with globules of yolk and adhere tightly to the subjacent yolk mass. The central zone is more translucent and is referred to as the *area pellucida.* It is this portion of the blastoderm whence the embryo proper subsequently arises. The marginal zone is the *area opaca.* It develops into the *yolk sac,* a highly vascular and complex structure completely surrounding the yolk that mediates the transfer of nutrients from yolk to embryo via the blood-vascular system, which arises later (Figure 3·11).

The hypoblast of the early blastoderm is prospective endoderm; the epiblast comprises the future ectoderm and mesoderm and contributes some endoderm also. At one end of the *area pellucida,* the future posterior end of the embryo, there is a greater density of cells than elsewhere. As gastrulation progresses, cells of the upper layer move posteriorly and toward the midline, forming a longitudinal structure called the *primitive streak.* This comprises an elongate groove with elevated sides, the *primitive groove,* which deepens anteriorly to form the *primitive pit.* The streak ends anteriorly in a cluster of cells in

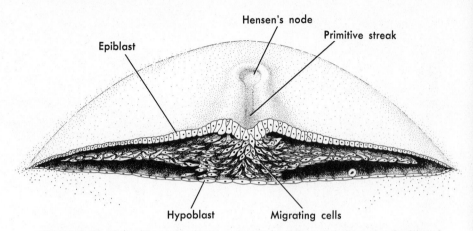

Figure 3·10. Three-dimensional representation of the migration of cells through the primitive streak to contribute the mesoderm and some endoderm. [Adapted from B. I. Balinsky, *An Introduction to Embryology*, 2d ed., Philadelphia; Saunders, 1965, p. 207.]

front of the pit, the *primitive knot* or *Hensen's node* (Figures 3·10 and 3·11).

As cells of the epiblast converge upon the primitive streak, they pass through the primitive groove, some contributing to the hypoblast but most spreading out as a middle layer interposed between epiblast and hypoblast; the middle layer is the mesoderm (Figure 3·10). Apparently, cells developing in the region of Hensen's node contribute the notochord, which extends forward from the node as a condensation of cells; during early stages it is called the *head process* (Figure 3·11F). Critical evidence for the invagination of mesoderm through the primitive streak has been obtained recently from experiments in which the passage of radioactively labeled cells of the epiblastic layer has been traced through the streak and into the embryonic heart (Figure 3·12). Cells of the epiblast that do not invaginate through the primitive streak remain as the ectoderm.

The *area pellucida* elongates (Figure 3·13A). The streak moves

Figure 3·11. Formation of the primitive streak and head process in the chick embryo. A: The isolated blastoderm of the unincubated egg, showing the peripheral *area opaca* and the central *area pellucida*; a somewhat denser concentration of cells, the embryonic shield, marks the posterior side of the *area pellucida*. **B, C, and D:** Successively later stages in the formation of the primitive streak. **E.** The definitive primitive streak. **F:** Head-process stage; the material whence the notochord arises extends anteriorly from Hensen's node as the head process. [**A, B, D, E,** and **F** from N. T. Spratt, in *J. Exptl. Zool.,* 120:110, fig. 1a,b,c; 122, fig. 5; 123, fig. 6. **C** from N. T. Spratt, in *J. Exptl. Zool.,* 103:274, fig. 7. By courtesy of Dr. Spratt and permission of The Wistar Institute.]

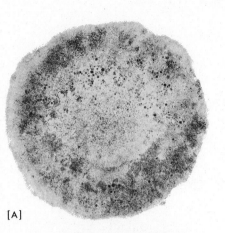
[A]

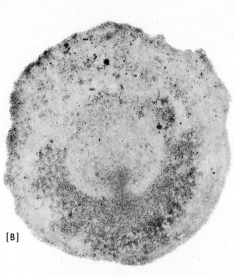
[B]

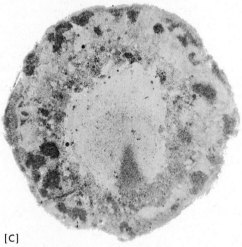
[C]

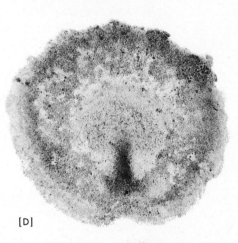
[D]

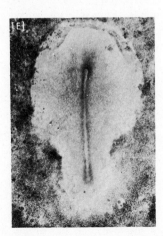
[E]

[F]

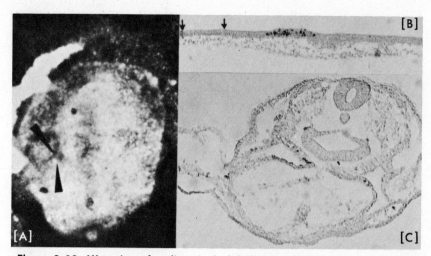

Figure 3·12. Migration of radioactively labeled precardiac cells in the chick embryo into the primitive streak and their subsequent appearance in the heart primordium. A: Living embryo at the primitive-streak stage bearing a graft (arrows) of epiblast cells from a radioactively labeled (tritiated thymidine) donor epiblast. B: Cross section of a similar embryo, showing entrance of labeled cells (dark spots) into the primitive streak; original position of graft shown by arrows. C: Cross section through the same embryo shown in A, but several hours later, after the heart has formed; labeled cells are seen in the heart and other nearby mesoderm. [From G. C. Rosenquist and R. L. DeHaan, in *Carnegie Contribs. Embryol.*, 38:113–121, 1966, by courtesy of the authors and permission of the Carnegie Institution of Washington.]

posteriorly as cells continue to pass through to the inside. This movement is called *regression*, and it comprises, first, a relative displacement posteriorly of the entire streak and, second, shortening of the streak itself. The regressing streak leaves behind it progressively more posterior levels of mesoderm interposed between hypoblast and epiblast, with the notochord, or head process, directly in the midline (Figure 3·13B). Structures of the embryonic axis then appear in anteroposterior order, directly following the posterior movement of the streak, so that by the time regression is complete, the longitudinal axis of the embryo is laid out anterior to Hensen's node (Figure 3·13C).

PRIMATES

Cleavage and gastrulation in human beings, other primates, and most mammals must take place with the concomitant elaboration of systems for attachment of the embryo to the wall of the maternal uterus. A brief sketch of the initial phases of development in human beings and allied primates will illustrate formation of these systems.

The egg, essentially yolkless, is fertilized in the Fallopian tube as it moves toward the uterus, and the first cleavage division takes place in less than twenty-four hours. It is meridional and unequal. Succeeding cleavages are somewhat irregular, but there is soon formed a more or less solid ball of cells, the *morula.* Fluid accumulates in the spaces between the cells, and by the time about one hundred cells are present, the embryo comprises a fluid-filled vesicle, the *blastocyst,* with a small mass of cells, the *inner cell mass,* occupying a part of its

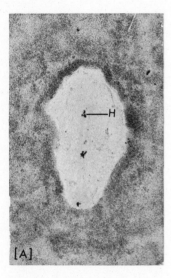

[A]

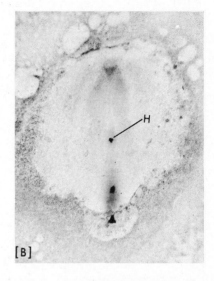

[B]

Figure 3·13. Regression and shortening of the primitive streak in the chick embryo. A: The blastoderm at the stage of the definitive primitive streak; clumps of finely divided carbon particles mark Hensen's node (*H*) and the middle and posterior end of the streak. **B:** After several hours, the head process has formed anterior to the node, and the streak has moved posteriorly. **C:** Shortening and regression of the streak continue as longitudinal axis of the embryo appears anterior to it. [From N. T. Spratt, in *J. Exptl. Zool.,* 104:77, fig. 4a,b,c. By courtesy of Dr. Spratt and permission of The Wistar Institute.]

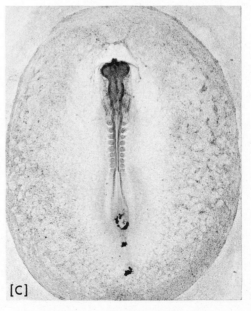

[C]

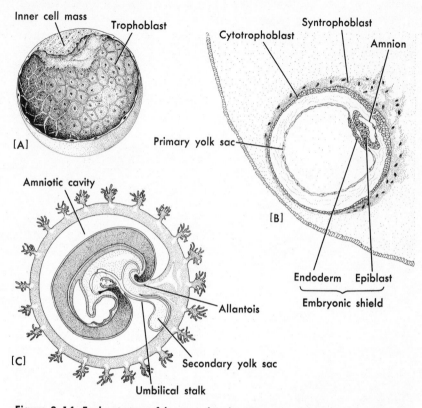

Figure 3·14. Early stages of human development. A: The blastocyst, comprising trophoblast and inner cell mass. **B:** Differentiation of the trophoblast into syntrophoblast and cytotrophoblast during implantation; formation of the embryonic shield, amnion, and yolk sac. **C:** The embryo floating in a cushion of amniotic fluid and attached to the umbilical stalk. [**A** and **C** redrawn from B. M. Patten, *Foundations of Embryology* 2d ed., New York: McGraw-Hill, 1964, pp. 123, 331; **B** is an interpretation of the structure of a twelve-day embryo based on a photograph by A. T. Hertig and J. Rock, in *Carnegie Contribs. Embryol.* 29:127–156, 1941.]

periphery (Figure 3·14A). The outer layer of the vesicle is called the *trophoblast*.

The trophoblast attaches to the wall of the uterus. Its cells multiply rapidly and invade the uterine epithelium in the initial stages of implantation. After nine days, the entire blastocyst is imbedded in the uterine wall. While this is going on, the lower cells of the inner mass arrange themselves into a plate of cells, the *primary endoderm,* that forms the digestive tract. The remaining cells of the inner mass flatten into a disk. Between the embryonic disk and the overlying trophoblast a fluid-filled cavity appears. This cavity is called the *amniotic cavity* (Figure 3·14B). The walls of the cavity, the *amnion,* expand, enveloping the entire embryo and surrounding it with a liquid cushion, the *amniotic fluid* (Figure 3·14C).

The embryonic disk, which forms the floor of the amniotic cavity, and its underlying endoderm are comparable to the epiblast and the hypoblast, respectively, in the *area pellucida* of the chick embryo. From the embryonic disk and its endoderm the entire embryo develops. Also, it appears that in the mammal the mesoderm develops the same way it does in the chick, namely by invagination of epiblast cells through the primitive streak, which regresses posteriorly as the body axis forms ahead of it.

4

Morphogenetic Processes

WITH THE COMPLETION of gastrulation, the embryo has accomplished a major step toward becoming a functionally independent organism. Its tissues are arranged in a manner roughly corresponding to their definitive relationships, and, with the appropriate shaping and molding of the germ layers, the characteristic form of the organism will develop. This chapter concerns the processes that operate during the emergence of that form.

At first glance the task of analyzing the emergence of the definitive body form from the three-layered gastrula seems almost insurmountable. Yet it is quite possible to resolve the accomplishment of the final shaping of the organism into a number of elementary morphogenetic processes affecting the germ layers individually or jointly. These processes are relatively easy to outline, even though their underlying mechanisms may remain partially or wholly obscure.

Outstanding among these processes are the formation of tissue folds, including invaginations and evaginations of cellular layers; fusion, detachment, or separation of cells, groups of cells, and cell layers; local aggregations and condensations of cells; cellular multiplication or local proliferation; migration of cells from their sites of origin; differential growth; and differential death. The changes in form shown by various embryos during their development (Figures 4·1 and 4·2) reveal many external events that might be attributed to the occurrence of these processes. I shall use principally the embryos of amphibians and birds to illustrate the ways in which these processes contribute to the morphogenetic preformance of each of the germ layers.

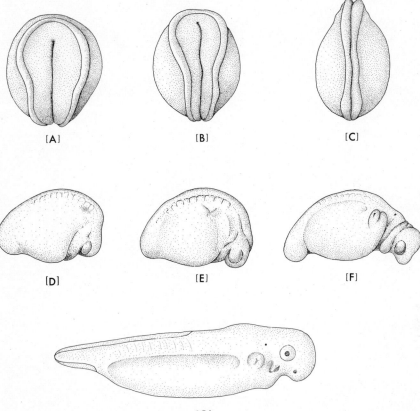

[A]   [B]   [C]

[D]   [E]   [F]

[G]

Figure 4·1. A series of stages in the development of the amphibian *Amblystoma maculatum*. [Adapted from V. Hamburger, *A Manual of Experimental Embryology*, Chicago: The University of Chicago Press, 1942, pp. 202–204.]

Ectoderm

It is appropriate to begin with the ectoderm, for it is the layer that contributes the first major morphogenetic change following gastrulation. In the amphibian embryo, the cells of the future dorsal side become condensed into a compact pear-shaped plate with raised edges. This plate is the *neural plate* and its edges are the *neural folds* (Figures 4·1A and 4·3); the folds rise and fuse over the center of the original plate. Condensation, folding, and fusion thus are mechanisms whereby the neural plate is transformed into the *neural tube*. The latter, which is destined to form the brain and spinal cord, is detached from the overlying ectoderm; groups of cells that comprise the *neural crest* are detached from the fusing corners of the folds. Neural-crest

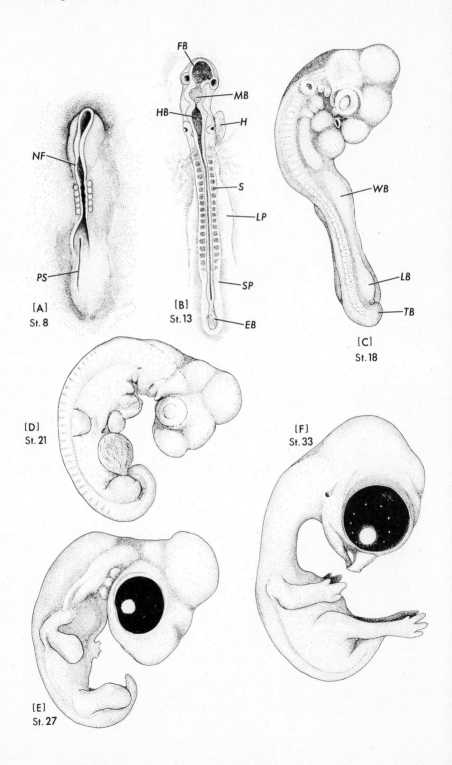

[A] St. 8

[B] St. 13

[C] St. 18

[D] St. 21

[E] St. 27

[F] St. 33

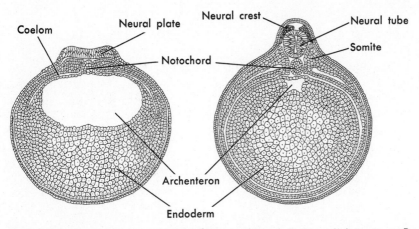

Figure 4·3. Neurulation in the amphibian embryo. A: Neural-plate stage. B: Closed neural tube. [Adapted from A. F. Huettner, *Comparative Embryology of the Vertebrates*, New York: Macmillan, 1949, p. 88.]

cells migrate extensively; they move to all parts of the body, forming pigment cells, which give color to the skin and its derivatives (e.g., hair, feathers, scales). They also form, among other things, cartilages of the jaw, spinal and sympathetic neurons, and some neurons of the cranial ganglia (Figure 4·4).

Shortly after the neural tube is formed, the future forebrain region evaginates on left and right sides, forming the bulging *optic vesicles* (Figure 4·5). These push through the loose mesoderm of the head and make contact with the head ectoderm. The ectodermal cells then elongate perpendicularly to the zone of contact, forming on each side a thickening (*placode*), the future lens of the eye, which then invaginates as a vesicle and detaches from the overlying ectoderm. As it detaches, the optic vesicle reverses its outward bulge and invaginates, forming the *optic cup* (*eyecup*), which accommodates the invaginating lens. The lining of the eyecup subsequently forms the retina.

Two placodes arise on each side of the head anteriorly and then invaginate to form the nasal grooves, whence develop the sensory epithelium of the olfactory organ. Two others form posteriorly and then invaginate to form the *otic vesicles*, which ultimately contribute the

Figure 4·2. Stages in the development of the chick embryo. Numbers indicate developmental stages in the Hamburger-Hamilton series. EB, end bud; FB, forebrain; H, heart; HB, hindbrain; LB, leg bud; MB, midbrain; NF, neural fold; PS, primitive streak; S, somite; SP, segmental plate; TB, tail bud. [Stages 8 and 14 after Keibel and Abraham as adapted from B. I. Balinsky, *An Introduction to Embryology*, Philadelphia: Saunders, 1965, p. 213. Stages 18, 21, 27, and 33 are interpretative drawings of photographs of corresponding stages in V. Hamburger and H. L. Hamilton, in *J. Morphol.*, 88:49–92, 1951.]

inner ear. Other ectodermal thickenings appear in the nearby head region and contribute to ganglia of the cranial nerves. The ganglionic placodes do not invaginate as vesicular structures, but cells detach from them, migrate centrally, and set up foci of *neuroblasts,* prospective nerve cells of the ganglia. Neural-crest cells also contribute neuroblasts to some of these ganglia. Migration and aggregation are very important for establishing future nerve cells in morphological positions essential to their future functional relationships.

Mechanisms similar to those that form the nervous system and sense

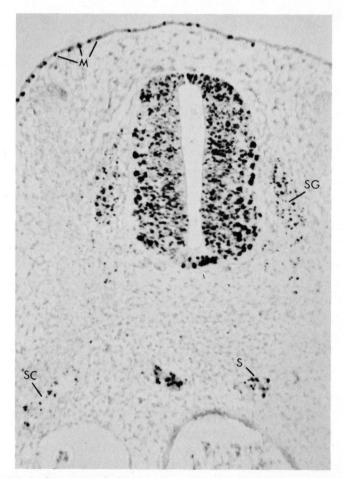

Figure 4·4. Radioautograph showing the migration of labeled neural-crest cells to form melanoblasts (M), neuroblasts of the sensory ganglia (SG), sympathetic neuroblasts (S), and sheath cells of a motor nerve(SC). The neural tube with neural crests was exercised from the trunk region of a chick embryo with radioactively labeled nuclei (tritiated thymidine) and grafted to a nonlabeled host in place of its own neural tube and crests. [From J. A. Weston, in *Developmental Biol.* 6:279–310, 1963. By courtesy of Dr. Weston and permission of Academic Press, Inc., New York.]

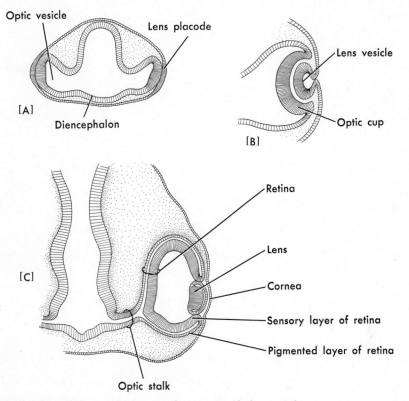

Figure 4·5. Early stages in morphogenesis of the vertebrate eye as seen in stylized cross sections through the embryonic forebrain.

organs also occur in structuring other derivatives of the ectodermal layer, notably the integument and its derivatives. Condensations and local proliferations participate in formation of feathers, hairs, and glands of the skin (Figure 4·6); the eyelids are formed by integumentary folds that first fuse, covering the eye, and later break through when cells at the line of fusion keratinize and die. Such processes, however, provide the finishing touches; the ectoderm makes its major contribution to body shape by forming the nervous system. Other major factors in achieving the definitive form of the organism must be sought in the other body layers.

Mesoderm

As already noted, for many embryos a main component of gastrulation is the massive inturning, or invagination, of mesoderm through a blastopore or primitive streak. Once within, the mesoderm constitutes a massive middle layer that eventually contributes the great bulk of the body, thus determining its form to a major extent.

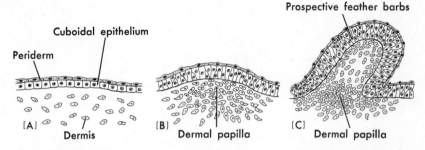

Figure 4·6. Origin of the feather in the chick embryo. A: Prospective skin prior to feather formation. **B:** Condensation of mesoderm forming the dermal papilla; onset of epidermal thickening. **C:** Proliferation of ectoderm and mesoderm to form the feather germ.

Upon the completion of gastrulation in the frog and higher vertebrates, the mesoderm in the dorsal midline of the neurula detaches itself from the lateral mesoderm to form the rodlike notochord, which runs almost the full length of the embryo (Figure 4·3). This structure lies directly beneath the neural tube and provides a rigid support along the embryonic axis. The notochord persists as the only skeleton-like support in the Protochordata, but in higher vertebrates it mostly degenerates and contributes only to the intervertebral disks.

Lateral to the notochord on each side, the mesodermal cells of the segmental plate condense into a row of tissue blocks, the *somites*. These subsequently form the vertebral column and the musculature and dermis of the dorsal side and, possibly depending on the organism, contribute to the ribs. The segmental arrangement of the somites is easily seen in early embryos (Figures 4·1 and 4·2). It is thought by some to reflect the primitive metameric arrangement of body parts in presumed invertebrate ancestors of the vertebrates. In the vertebrates,

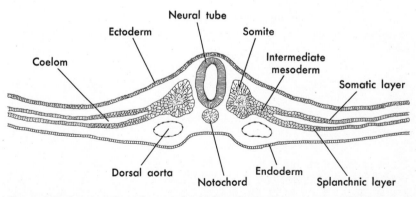

Figure 4·7. Cross section of an early chick embryo, illustrating the relationships of the germ layers.

of course, metamerism is largely lost, but aspects of it are retained in the segmental arrangement of the body-wall musculature in the lower vertebrates and in the serially ordered vertebrae, each of which is contributed by cells from the posterior face of one somite and the anterior face of the succeeding one.

Lateral to the somites, there is a narrow intermediate zone of mesoderm; beyond this zone, the mesoderm separates into two layers, an outer somatic layer and an inner splanchnic layer (Figures 3·5, 4·3, and 4·7). The intermediate mass is the chief source of the urogenital organs and adrenal cortex. The splanchnic layer contributes the heart, invests the digestive tract, and forms the mesenteries; the somatic layer contributes the peritoneum, the muscular layers of the body wall, and the paired appendages.

The shaping of the appendages provides a good example of the interplay of a number of morphogenetic mechanisms. Cells of the somatic mesoderm aggregate beneath the future limb ectoderm and undergo rapid proliferation, forming a conical (in urodeles, for example) or paddle-shaped (human; chick, see Figure 4·2) projection from the body wall called the limb bud. In birds, for which the process has been extensively analyzed, the shaping of this projection into the definitive form of a forelimb or hind limb is accomplished chiefly by differential growth, aided by differential cellular death. Growth contributes the bulk of the limb and blocks out its general form; but as the limb buds elongate, waves of cellular death sweep

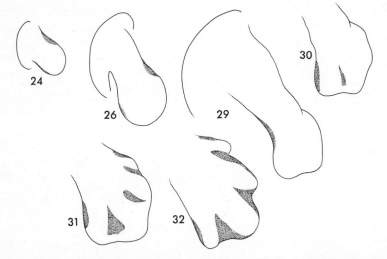

Figure 4·8. The topographic distribution of cellular deaths during development of the leg bud in the chick embryo. Numbers refer to developmental stages of the chick in the Hamburger-Hamilton series. [V. Hamburger and H. L. Hamilton, in *J. Morphol.*, 88:49–92, 1951.]

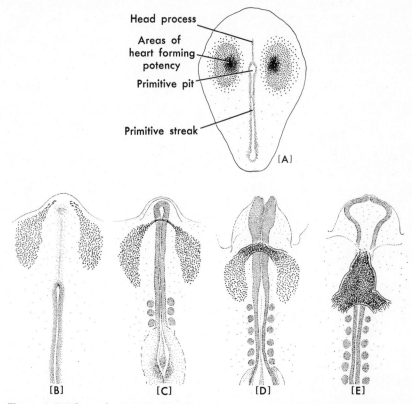

Head process

Areas of
heart forming
potency

Primitive pit

Primitive streak

[A]

[B]   [C]   [D]   [E]

Figure 4·9. Bilateral origin and medial movement of heart-forming cells during early stages in the development of the chick embryo. A: Area of heart-forming potency in the head-process blastoderm (stage 5) as revealed by grafting experiments. **B to E:** The positions occupied by heart-forming cells at Hamburger-Hamilton stages 6−, 8−, 8+, and 10+, respectively. [**A** adapted from M. E. Rawles, in *Physiol. Zool.,* 16:22–42, 1943; the remaining figures adapted from R. L. DeHaan, in *Acta Embryol et Morphol. Exptl.,* 6:26–38, 1963.]

along the mesoderm of the anterior and posterior edges of the appendages, and their refined contours emerge as the waves pass. This process reaches a climax in the erosion of the interdigital tissues, which apparently aids in the sculpturing of the toes (Figure 4·8).

The origin of the heart is of considerable interest. In the chick, the future heart-forming cells lie on either side of the primitive streak at its anterior end (Figure 4·9). These cells detach from the splanchnic mesoderm and aggregate in small clusters. The clusters migrate toward the midline, gliding on the underlying layer of endoderm. As the anterior end of the embryo is undercut from the yolk by the formation of the head fold, the clusters from each side arrange themselves in the form of a loosely structured tube. The tubes from each side fuse, beginning anteriorly and extending for a distance posteriorly. They make a single tube that elongates and is thrown into folds that demark the various heart regions.

Endoderm

The development history of the endoderm importantly includes long-distance migration of the primordial germ cells, prominent fold-ings, and a number of evaginations from the digestive tube. In the bird and mammal, the embryonic body is undercut by anterior, lateral, and posterior folds. These folds involve all three germ layers, and thus the endoderm appears as the innermost tube of the three-layered embryo. In urodeles, as noted in Chapter 3, folds of endoderm rise from the sides of the floor of the archenteron and fuse dorsally to roof the cavity of the digestive tract.

The primordial germ cells are of endodermal origin. They arise at

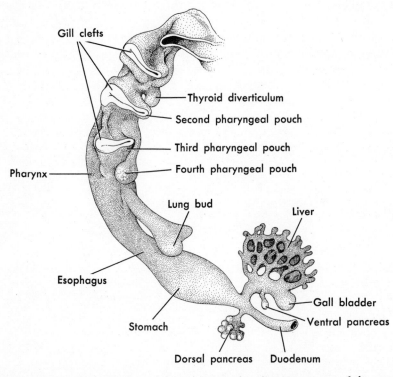

Figure 4·10. Major endodermal derivatives in the alimentary tract of the mammal. [Adapted from various sources, including G. L. Weller, in *Carnegie Contribs. Embryol.*, 24:93–139, 1933; and W. W. Ballard, *Comparative Anatomy and Embryology*, New York: Ronald, 1964, p. 463.]

some distance from their final site. In anuran amphibians, they apparently originate deep in the yolky endoderm and are carried to the roof of the gut by the morphogenetic movements of gastrulation and neurulation; thence they migrate to the gonads. In the chick, they take their origin from a germinal crescent at the anterior margin of the very early blastoderm and subsequently travel to the gonads via the blood stream. In the mammal, they originate in the yolk sac posteriorly and then travel via the gut and dorsal mesentery to the gonads. When the primordial germ cells are deleted experimentally or eliminated through genetic mutation, sterile gonads form.

Evaginations of the digestive tube give rise to the major endodermal organs (Figure 4·10). In the pharyngeal region, paired pouches bulge out laterally, meet ectodermal invaginations, and form gill slits. The pouches persist and become functional in the respiratory apparatus of the lower vertebrates, but they form, among other things, the Eustachian tube, thymus, and parathyroid glands in the higher chordates. In the same general area, an evagination in the ventral midline anteriorly marks the beginning of the thyroid gland, and another gives rise to the lung bud. Further posteriorly, at the level of the future duodenum, other evaginations initiate development of the liver, pancreas, and gall bladder. These organs are not, of course, purely endodermal in their final state; mesoderm invests them and supplies blood vessels and a framework of connective tissue that binds each organ into its definitive shape.

Principles of Development: The Conceptual Framework for Developmental Events

ONE MIGHT CONTINUE almost indefinitely to adduce numerous data about the events, the observable phenomena, of embryogenesis to the theme of the what, where, and when of development. But this procedure would rapidly reach a point of diminishing returns in understanding how the form and function of the new individual emerge from the fertilized egg. It is necessary, therefore, to undertake another aspect of the problem of development, namely the synthesis of a significant conceptual framework from the factual materials that have been learned and some others that may be introduced as appropriate.

A conceptual framework is constructed from principles, statements of general truth derived by inductive reasoning from facts, or data. Thus the mind formulates a *principle of development* in recognition of the interrelatedness of a group of facts about development. The principle gives to these facts a unity and meaning that, alone, they lack; it enhances understanding of developmental events by putting them in meaningful relationships with each other.

But a principle of development has, of itself, no analytic value; it tells nothing about the nature of developmental events, their mode of operation, or the causal relationships between them. For example, we may speak of the *principle of induction* with reference to the role of one embryonic structure in determining what another shall form, but enunciation of the principle tells us nothing of the means whereby various inductions are carried out.

Mechanisms, on the other hand, are cause-and-effect relationships that determine that certain events shall occur. Understanding the mechanisms underlying developmental events is the goal of most modern analytic embryology. Hopefully, the recognition of developmental principles enables the better formulation of problems concerning basic mechanisms; and conversely, the solution of analytic problems should lead to the induction of new principles. Thus our understanding of development requires a knowledge of both its principles, which give developmental events their meaning in relation to other events, and its mechanisms, which enable us to understand the causality of these events and to control their occurrence. In this chapter we shall give special attention to a few of the major principles that have emerged from the study of embryonic development.

Differentiation

In embryogenesis there arise different organs and systems of organs, each made up of tissues in various combinations and arrangements. And each of these tissues comprises certain kinds of cells that are clearly recognizable as different from other kinds: the cells of skeletal muscle are quite unlike those of the liver; brain cells are distinctive from cells that line the intestine; there are red blood cells and a variety of white blood cells, and these are all different from fat cells, skin cells, and so on. Moreover, each kind of cell has its own specialized function, its biochemical individuality, and its morphogenetic assignment. Thus it is evident that whereas all cells of the mature organism arose from one fertilized ovum by repeated divisions and thus presumably inherited the same basic biochemical endowment, they became different during the course of development. Under the *principle of differentiation* we order those phenomena and ideas that relate to the processes whereby cells achieve during development their distinctive biochemical, structural, and functional characteristics. Indeed, most of the facts that have been learned about development could be ordered about this principle, for almost every aspect of development contributes to, and is characterized by, the acquisition of differentness. Moreover, many of the principles we shall consider also apply to the origin and properties of differentiated cells, though they will be treated individually for convenience and greater emphasis.

Some very important subordinate principles can be treated under the general principle of differentiation. One of these is the principle of *discreteness of differentiation*. Simple observation shows that differentiation produces discrete, distinct cell types, that is, discontinuous kinds of cell populations, each with its distinguishing features. Liver cells are clearly distinct from cells of skeletal muscle, and no liver cell shows the striated pattern found in muscle; cells of the thyroid gland are different from those of skin and brain, and so on.

Another subordinate principle is that of the *stability of the differ-*

entiated state. By and large, cells that have differentiated to a particular terminal state are incapable, under ordinary circumstances, of transforming into other types of cells—bone cells do not become muscle cells, epithelial cells do not transform into cartilage cells, and so on. But for many kinds of cells the stability of the differentiated state is a matter of degree; some cells are quite stable as long as their normal environment is unaltered. Thus in urodeles the pigmented cells of the iris of the eye are unchanging unless the lens of the eye is removed. If this is done, however, the cells of the dorsal margin of the iris lose their pigment and bud off a bit of tissue that grows and transforms into a new lens; that is, given the right circumstances, cells of the dorsal iris margin develop a structure they would otherwise never form.

The question of the stability of differentiation has been the subject of a good deal of controversy, much of it originating in semantics. For example, may one call a cell differentiated if it can transform, or should only those cells that never transform be considered differentiated? Would not any nucleated cell be capable of transformation if placed under the proper conditions? These questions reflect inadequacies in our definitions of the differentiated state. The character of differentiation must be sought in the genetic endowment of the cell under consideration. This will be explained in Chapter 6; for the present, suffice it to say that there are no a priori reasons to consider that a cell possessed of its normal complement of nuclear and cytoplasmic machinery could not transform into another kind of cell. Moreover, cells probably differ greatly in their ability to change from one differentiated state into another. It is a part of the task of the student of development to learn what factors determine that a particular state of more or less rigid stability shall be attained by a cell.

Because of its importance and current interest, we should also consider another principle that is subordinate to differentiation, namely the principle of *specificity of cellular association.* I have already noted that embryonic cells, even though they may be extremely mobile during early stages (e.g., neural-crest cells, heart-forming cells, primordial germ cells), do eventually settle down into relatively intimate association with other cells in the construction of a tissue or organ. Thereafter, they do not normally reject their neighbors and move away. Exceptions are found, of course, in the cells of the circulatory system, whose normal business it is to move about, and in the cells of malignant cancers. This suggests that cells must be equipped with some sorts of biochemical specificities that determine whether a stable or unstable relationship with neighboring cells shall be achieved. Such *recognition signals* are very important, for they determine the

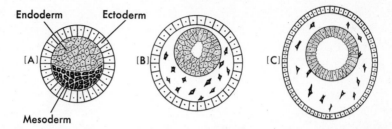

Figure 5·1. Artificial combinations of ectoderm, endoderm, and mesoderm from the amphibian gastrula arrange themselves with the mesoderm interposed between an ectodermal cover and an inner, intestine-like vesicle of endoderm. **A, B,** and **C** show successive stages in the process. [Adapted from J. Holtfreter, in B. H. Willier and J. M. Oppenheimer (eds.), *Foundations of Experimental Embryology,* Englewood Cliffs, N.J.: Prentice-Hall, 1964, p. 201.]

relative affinities of various types of cells for those of their own and other kinds and thus govern to a considerable degree how cells may be assembled into tissues and organs.

The notion of relative affinities is well illustrated by experiments in which fragments of the amphibian gastrula are grown in appropriate salt solutions in glass vessels. If one wraps a fragment of gastrula endoderm and a small bit of mesoderm in a larger piece of gastrula ectoderm, the cells of the different layers arrange themselves always in a very characteristic manner: the endoderm moves to a central position, separating away from the ectoderm, and forms a hollow vesicle that looks in cross section like intestinal epithelium (Figure 5·1) ; the mesoderm interposes itself as a layer between the endoderm and ectoderm, the latter forming an epithelial ball surrounding the other two components. In combinations of only two kinds of gastrula tissue, one finds that the mesoderm is able to show an affinity for both ectoderm and endoderm,. whereas the other two components reject each other.

These differences in tissue affinity persist into later life, as has been shown in experiments on urodele larvae. When one makes a wound in the flank of the larva by excising a bit of epidermis, the cells of the cut edge begin to move across the mesodermal wound bed, towing their neighbors behind them. When the advancing cells from one side of the wound meet those from the other side, their migratory movement ceases and the edges fuse smoothly. If one places on the wound bed a smaller piece of skin ectoderm from another area of the embryo, the ectoderm of flank and graft move toward each other, meet, and fuse smoothly, so that the grafted skin is incorporated into the flank area. It is as though the ectodermal cells from different regions recognize each other and are cued by this recognition to cease their movements and to associate in a stable configuration.

Exploratory grafts of this kind show that ectoderm of the flank recognizes and associates smoothly with ectodermal epithelia from any region of the body; even the cornea of the eye and the oral epithelium are acceptable. This is far from the case, however, when the graft is taken from a tissue of endodermal origin, such as esophagus or intestine. In such instances, the spreading ectoderm simply continues its migration, the cells first piling up briefly at the edge of the foreign graft, then tunneling beneath it and displacing it to the outside so that it is shed. The ectodermal edges of the wound continue their migration until they meet, whereupon they fuse smoothly as they come to rest.

The recognition signals likewise work for isolated cells. One may illustrate this by separating the cells of the five-day embryonic chick heart by treating them with the enzyme trypsin in a calcium- and magnesium-free medium and then mixing them randomly with similarly isolated cartilage-forming mesenchymal cells of the limb bud. When the combined cells are compacted into a coherent mass by gentle gyratory swirling and then placed in a suitable nutrient environment, they engage in more or less random movements for a considerable period but eventually stabilize in a characteristic manner, forming a rounded tissue mass in which the limb-bud cells are located centrally, form cartilage, and are surrounded by heart cells. This suggests, first, that the two cell types preferentially adhere to those of their own kind, and second, that cartilage cells show a greater affinity for each other than do heart cells for their own kind. The result we call *cell sorting*. If one similarly mixes embryonic chick liver cells and heart cells, the heart cells lump together and exclude the liver cells, which cohere in a layer around them. Presumably heart cells have stronger affinities for each other than do liver cells, and thus they take the central position.

These results suggest that prospective limb-cartilage cells, heart cells, and liver cells have affinities for their own kinds with decreasing strength in the order named. If so, we would expect that the combination of liver and limb cells would lead to the segregation of the latter kind internally, with the liver surrounding. That is the case. Moreover, numerous combinations of cells from various embryonic tissues have been tested in this manner, and on the basis of these tests, one can arrange the tissues in strict order of their cohesiveness to their own kind.

The problems issuing from these phenomena and the associated affinities and sorting-out behavior are many and are far from being solved. Recognition of this aspect of cellular behavior has considerably advanced our understanding of embryonic development, however, for it has given us a basis for understanding something further about the synthesis of tissues and organs.

Determination

Behavioral tests show that before an organ or tissue achieves its definitive form and function—before its component cells assume the morphology or exercise the biochemical tasks that are the signs of their
differentiated state—the system already possesses the capacity to achieve
its morphogenetic goal in isolation from its normal surroundings, provided it has adequate nourishment and the opportunity for gaseous
exchange. As an example, let us consider the wing-forming region of
the chick embryo. The wing arises from the lateral body wall at the
levels of the fourteenth to nineteenth somites at about sixty hours of
incubation (Figure 5·2). If one extirpates this portion of the body
wall at forty-eight hours and transplants it to a site that provides a
proper vascular supply (e.g., the chorioallantoic membrane of an
older embryo—this is not a part of the embryo proper, but serves as a
membrane for gaseous exchange and a site for the deposit of nitrog-
enous wastes), it will grow into a rather well-developed wing. We
say, therefore, that the wing-forming region was *determined* at the
time of operation. One observes a great many cases in which an organ
or tissue primordium behaves in isolation as though committed to a
course of differentiation in advance of its actually achieving the cyto-

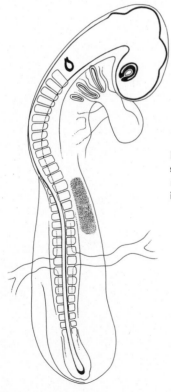

**Figure 5·2. Chick embryo after approximately
sixty hours of incubation.** The body wall on the
right side is shaded in the prospective wing-forming region.

logical and biochemical characteristics of the differentiated state. From such observations we induce the general *principle of determination.*

Presumably, there is a time when a system under consideration is not yet committed to its particular fate—i.e., a time when it is undetermined. The limb-forming regions of the chick embryo are apparently determined as early as one can locate them, for they develop into recognizable appendages even when isolated at very young stages. But for many systems the time of determination can be established with some precision, the most famous case being that of the nervous system of the amphibian, which becomes determined during the course of gastrulation. If one isolates a bit of the prospective neural ectoderm from a salamander blastula and grafts it to the belly region of another embryo, it will form only belly skin; but when the graft of ectoderm is taken from an embryo that has completed gastrulation and is similarly positioned on another embryo, it differentiates as neural tissue.

Dependent Differentiation: Induction

The commitment of a tissue or organ to a particular developmental fate is often dependent on relationships established with surrounding tissues. The *dependent differentiation* of the amphibian neural tube is a case in point. It receives its assignment—becomes determined—during gastrulation, and responsibility for this has been laid to action of the archenteron roof, i.e., the mesoderm that invaginates through the dorsal lip of the blastopore. If invagination is prevented, as by treatment of the blastula with lithium ions (Li^{++}), the ectoderm that normally becomes neural tube forms only an epidermal vesicle; more definitively, if a bit of archenteron roof (even before invagination) is grafted to a blastula so that it comes to lie beneath prospective belly skin, the latter then forms a neural tube (Figure 5·3). In cases where determination of a developmental end point is dependent upon association with an adjoining tissue, we speak of an *embryonic induction.*

An induction occurs whenever two tissues of dissimilar developmental origin become associated and there emerges as a consequence a more or less stable differentiation in one or both tissues that persists even after the association is terminated. In many experimental situations, only brief exposure to the inductor is required to fix firmly the developmental course of the reactant. There are many embryonic inductions, but they are not necessarily accomplished by the same means. We must distinguish the principle of induction from inductive mechanisms; the latter may be as varied as the inductions themselves, but we know very little about them.

The induction of neural tube by the archenteron roof is the first inductive event we recognize in amphibian development. The roof of

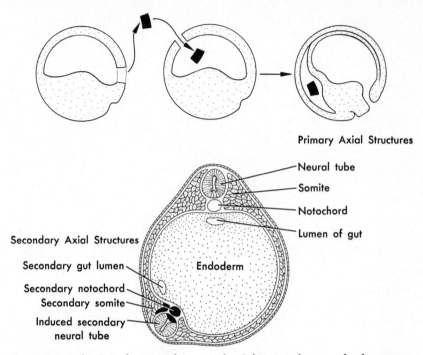

Figure 5·3. Induction of a secondary set of axial organs by a graft of prospective archenteron roof. Gastrulation movements of the host relegate the graft to a position subjacent to prospective belly ectoderm. Note that both ectodermal and mesodermal organs are induced by the graft, which may be distinguished from host tissues. [Adapted from H. Spemann and H. Mangold, in *Arch. mikroskop. Anat. und Entwicklungsmech.*, 100:599–638, 1924.]

the archenteron is thus often referred to as the *primary inductor* or even the *organizer* or *organization center* of the embryo. The latter terms emphasize the primacy of the neural induction; most subsequent inductions require the prior accomplishment of this one. Indeed, the amphibian embryo seems to prepare for neural induction as early as the time of fertilization, when it segregates the material that subsequently invaginates through the dorsal lip of the blastopore into a special zone of cortical protoplasm, the gray crescent (see Chapter 3). Pieces of gray crescent may actually be transplanted from one uncleaved egg or early embryo to another; becoming nucleated during cleavage, the pieces will invaginate at the time of gastrulation and induce a second neural tube in the ectoderm of the recipient.

To refer to the induction of the neural tube as primary is to imply that there are *secondary inductors, tertiary inductors,* and so on, in hierarchical array. For example, the brain, having been induced by archenteron roof, forms its various regional differentiations under the influence of head endoderm and mesoderm. The hindbrain induces overlying ectoderm to differentiate the ear placode, which then invaginates and, in turn, induces surrounding mesenchyme to form the cartilaginous auditory capsule. Another sequence that bears special mention is that of the formation of the eye. The optic vesicle, a differentiation of the midbrain, makes contact with head ectoderm, which then forms a lens; the lens invaginates; and the eyecup-lens complex then induces the overlying tissue to differentiate the transparent cornea and the surrounding mesoderm to form the sclerotic coat of the eyeball. These inductions have been examined experimentally; if a step in the sequence is omitted, the next steps fail to occur. Thus if the optic vesicle of the chick embryo is extirpated prior to its contact with head ectoderm, the lens fails to form. Without lens and optic vesicle, the other inductions associated with the development of the eye do not follow.

A number of the better-known secondary or tertiary inductions such as nasal-groove, otic-vesicle, lens, cornea, and so on involve ectodermal reactions. Experiments performed on chick and amphibian embryos show that these structures can be elicited in uncommitted ectoderm of various body regions as long as an appropriate inductor is present. We say that the ectoderm that can respond has *competence,* and one tends to the interpretation that the particular determination the competent ectodermal reacting system achieves is one that was specified in it by the inductor. Indeed, some would restrict the use of the term *induction* to cases in which the character of the response is prescribed by the inductor.

It is not always easy, however, to determine whether a particular inductor specifies the response or merely permits it. For the subordinate echelons of inductions, the repertory of permitted responses (competences) may be very limited, and the role of the inductor may be merely to throw the balance toward one of two alternative developmental pathways. In the amphibian embryo, lens competence is probably distributed over most ectodermal areas at early stages, for grafted optic vesicles elicit lens formation in the overlying ectoderm. However, lens competence is progressively restricted to the prospective lens placode as development proceeds. It is questionable whether the prospective lens has any developmental possibilities other than for lens and generalized epithelium at the time it is met by the optic vesicle.

Another difficulty arises from the fact that a particular differentiation that might be presumed to arise through a specific inductive action can sometimes be elicited by one or more kinds of grafts that bear no obvious relationship to the normal inductor. Thus the induction of lenses is reported to have been accomplished by grafts of fresh liver and by boiled heart. In the mouse, the secretory tubules of the definitive kidney are induced by the bud of the ureter in the mesoderm that surrounds it. The ureteric bud can induce the mesenchyme to make tubules even when the two components are separated and then recombined in tissue culture in glass vessels; more astonishingly, the bud can induce the mesenchyme to make tubules even if the components are separated by thin filters that bar cellular contact between them. Induction of kidney tubules in the prospective kidney mesoderm can also be carried out in vitro by epithelium of the salivary gland, fragments of spinal cord, limb mesenchyme, pancreatic epithelium, and other tissues. Thus whatever the nature of the stimulus provided by the ureteric bud to the prospective kidney mesoderm, it is apparently not specific to the bud but is a property that may be exercised by many tissues, at least under the conditions provided by tissue culture.

There seems to be a high degree of specificity, on the other hand, in the inductive relationships that determine the ectodermal derivatives of the integument. This can be shown clearly in birds; the feathers, which are ectodermal structures induced by the underlying skin mesoderm, are strikingly different on the various regions of their bodies. Determination of these regional differences apparently occurs very early, for if one transplants in the three-day chick embryo mesoderm from the prospective thigh-forming region of the leg bud to the surface of the wing bud in such a way that it is covered with wing ectoderm, the resulting bird, upon reaching adulthood, may show a patch of thigh feathers on its wing. Upper-wing mesoderm combined with leg ectoderm induces wing feathers, and foot-forming mesoderm combined in suitable grafts with wing ectoderm induces the latter to form scales and claws. The different inductors—thigh, upper wing, foot— thus have regionally specific inductive abilities, and early limb ectoderm is competent to respond to each of these inductors with a specific differentiation.

Genetic Limitations

In considering induction, it is important to bear in mind that the inductor can only elicit from the reacting system a response that is provided in the latter's genetic endowment. We are far from knowing just how inductors work, but it seems unlikely that they provide any information of a genetic kind; rather, they must provide a set of circumstances under which a particular aspect of the genetic repertory of the reacting system can come to expression.

It will be of value to adduce some cases of the genetically determined responses of induced systems. Let us first look at classic cases involving the specific configuration of head parts in the newt and the frog. The mouth armament of the frog comprises horny jaws, whereas the newt's head has calcareous teeth. The newt also has on its head ventrolateral outgrowths, the balancers, and the frog carries just behind the mouth, in a similar position, two suckers. All these structures are ectodermal derivatives that appear to be induced by the head endoderm. If some of the ectoderm of the future head region of an early gastrula of the newt is replaced by ectoderm of an early frog gastrula, the resulting chimera may show horny frog teeth and suckers on the modified newt head. In the reciprocal case, newt ectoderm developing in the head region of a frog embryo may form calcareous teeth and balancers. It is as though each ectoderm understands the inductive language of its own and foreign inductors, but can respond only according to its own genotype. The same principle shows in the fowl, where the structurally distinctive feathers of the silky-chicken mutant are formed from silky ectoderm underlaid by the mesodermal feather inductor from a normal bird.

One must recognize, however, that the genotype of a responding system may provide for responses never elicited by inductors of its own kind. This has been admirably shown in chimeric combinations of mesoderm and ectoderm of the upper beak in duck and chick embryos. When the ectodermless beak primordium of the duck is combined with reactive chick ectoderm, the latter responds by forming typical tooth ridges of duck type. These ridges normally do not form in chick ectoderm and are elicited neither in chick-chick combinations nor in ectoderm of duck reacting with upper-beak mesoderm of the chick. These results show that ectoderm of both chick and duck is competent to form tooth ridges, but the ability to elicit this response is possessed only by mesoderm of the duck. In this case the inductive system, not the reaction system, is genetically limited.

Reciprocal Action

In considering a particular induction, one tends to identify one component of the process as the initiating or action system and the other as the responding system. Thus we speak of induction of lens by optic vesicle, of neural tube by notochord, and so on. Yet when live tissues are in inductive association, it is more accurate to recognize that one is dealing with stimulus-response sequences acting in both directions; that is, there is *reciprocal action* between components of the inductive system. The effect of the induced system on the inductor is sometimes rather subtle, however, and often not readily recognized.

The principle of reciprocal action can be illustrated by the interaction of ectoderm and mesoderm in morphogenesis of the vertebrate limb. In the chick embryo, when the wing bud arises at sixty hours of

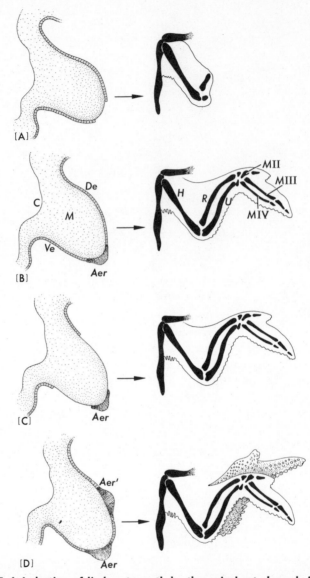

Figure 5·4. Induction of limb outgrowth by the apical ectodermal ridge in the chick embryo. On the left, schematic cross sections of the wing bud depicting various operations. On the right, the results obtained. **A:** Excision of the ridge results in deficiencies of terminal limb parts. **B:** In the presence of a normal ectodermal covering, the wing parts appear in their normal proximodistal sequence and pattern. **C:** Removal of the dorsal and ventral ectoderm permits outgrowth to continue as long as an apical ridge is present **D:** Grafting an extra ridge to the dorsal surface of the wing bud results in formation of two wings. Aer, apical ectodermal ridge; Aer', grafted apical ectodermal ridge; C, coelom; De, ectoderm of the dorsal face of the wing bud; H, humerus; M, mesenchymal core; R, radius; U, ulna; Ve, ectoderm of the ventral face of the wing bud. M II, M III, and M IV, metacarpals II, III, and IV, respectively.

incubation, the ectoderm at its apex thickens, forming an antero-posterior ridge. This is called the *apical ectodermal ridge*. It forms in the ectoderm in response to mesodermal induction, for when prospective wing mesoderm is grafted to a wound in the flank, the ectoderm that heals over it forms a ridge. Flank ectoderm loses its competence to give this response to mesodermal induction at about sixty-five hours of incubation. Mesoderm loses its capacity to induce at about the same time.

The apical ridge itself is now an inductor. If it is removed from the apex of the mesodermal bulge, limb development ceases. If the mesoderm of the limb primordium is adorned with two ridges by means of suitable microsurgical techniques, two limbs will grow out from the originally single primordium. The ectodermal ridge, therefore, is said to induce mesodermal outgrowth (Figure 5·4).

The story does not end here, however, for the growing mesoderm now reacts on the ectodermal ridge to keep it in a thick and inductively active configuration. It supplies a maintenance factor, not yet identified, that can pass through filters barring cellular contact; this factor keeps the apical ridge inductively active until the terminal parts of the limb are formed.

The analysis of limb morphogenesis has given us a considerable insight into the reciprocal nature of tissue interactions during development. It shows that interacting systems maintain, not a one-way communications system, but a dialogue, transmitting developmental cues in both directions and balancing and adjusting them so as to achieve the construction of a harmonious organ.

The Morphogenetic Field

A concept that brings order, though not explanation, to a great body of embryological data is that of the *morphogenetic field*. It is difficult to define a field in a way that is meaningful and acceptable to all biologists. The definition offered here will probably take on different shades of meaning according to the varying levels of scientific sophistication enjoyed by those who read it.

A morphogenetic field is the constellation of factors that determines that a part of an embryo shall engage in or have some commitment to follow a specific course of development. Thus one might refer to the chordamesoderm field as the set of properties that resides in a part of the amphibian embryo and determines that this part will invaginate, induce neural tube, and form notochord and associated mesodermal structures; the limb field would occupy that part of the embryo in which a set of activities has differentiated that confers the potency of limb formation and leads to that developmental end point.

The concept of the morphogenetic field has been evoked frequently

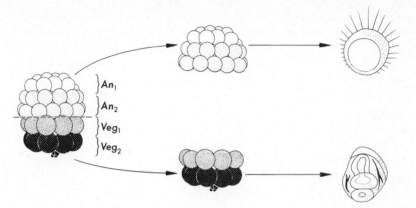

Figure 5·5. The morphogenesis of isolated animal and vegetal halves of the sea-urchin blastula. [Based on S. Horstadius, in *Bio. Revs.*, 14:132–179, 1939.]

in the analysis of sea-urchin development. The structure of the sea-urchin blastula was illustrated in Figure 3·1. If we separate the egg into animal ($an_1 + an_2$) and vegetal ($veg_1 + veg_2 +$ micromeres) halves, the isolated animal half forms a small hollow blastula almost entirely covered with long cilia. This structure develops no further and dies. The vegetal half likewise fails to survive, but it first forms a gut with rudimentary skeletal parts and an insufficient ectodermal covering; it lacks long cilia (Figure 5·5). We may designate as properties of the animal field the set of factors that leads to the formation of animal structures, namely the ectoderm and the long cilia of the apical tuft. And we designate as properties of the vegetal field factors that lead to formation of the skeletal parts and digestive tract. In the intact egg, the animal and vegetal fields are so balanced that a harmonious embryo develops. One may extend the vegetal field, however, by treatment of the embryo with Li^{++}, so that animal cells of the gastrula actually make vegetal structures and the ectoderm and the apical tuft of cilia are greatly reduced. Reciprocally, one may extend the animal field by treatment with NaSCN, causing the apical tuft to spread, vegetal cells to become animalized, and the gut to be reduced.

The high point of activity, or field center, of the vegetal field is the vegetal pole, where the micromeres are formed (Figure 3·1). If an isolated animal half is supplied only the micromeres from a vegetal half, some animal cells then make vegetal structures and a normal but smaller embryo is formed. If the animal cells are supplied the veg_2 ring of cells, the larva that forms may have a deficient gut and the apical tuft of the animal half will be extended. An animal half combined with the veg_1 ring forms very little gut and the apical tuft is much more extensive than normal. These considerations show that there is a gradient of vegetalizing activity that has its high point at the vegetal pole and progressively decreases in strength toward the animal pole; these and other experiments also suggest that the animal field has an opposite gradient with its high point at the animal pole and progressively diminishing activity toward the vegetal pole. One can actually combine two sea-urchin embryos to form one double-sized larva, otherwise normal, if they are grafted together with their animal-vegetal gradients coinciding.

Suppose we now bisect a sea-urchin blastula by a cut that passes through both animal and vegetal poles. Each meridional half-blastula will make a complete gastrula and larva, the animal and vegetal field centers shifting to the opposing geometric centers of the remaining portions of the original animal and vegetal gradients.

The experimental analysis of many morphogenetic fields reveals their characteristics: they have *strength,* as shown by the ability of organ fields to differentiate their structures in isolation and to incorporate surrounding cells and tissues into their morphogenetic patterns under other circumstances; they show *heteropolarity,* as reflected in gradients of the field strength along the three dimensions of space within the field; and they have *regulating ability,* in that the pattern of the whole field may be reconstituted from a part of the field, or a single field may be formed by the fusion of two fields. The property of regulating ability shows us that the field as a whole may have an irreversible commitment even though the fates of the cells that comprise it are not individually determined.

As development proceeds, reactions within the comprehensive fields leads to the establishment of smaller fields of increasing specialization, i.e., concerned with only limited patterns of differentiation. Thus the vegetal field breaks up into intestinal field, skeletal field, and so on; the discussion of induction and determination included examples of this. The chordamesoderm field induces the neural field which, itself, breaks up into smaller fields that may themselves be inductive. Close examination of one of the subordinate fields can illustrate that these fields have attributes parallel to those of the comprehensive fields.

Carefully cut and measured fragments of the very early blastoderm of the chick embryo have been transferred to the vascular chorioallantoic membrane of an older embryo and allowed to develop in order to learn their organ-forming potency. By referring the developmental performance of the grafts to landmarks on the blastoderm, the morphogenetic fields for various organs may be mapped. Thus shortly after gastrulation begins, regions of heart-forming potency may be located in paired oval areas on either side of the primitive pit (Figure 4·10A). As noted in Chapter 4, the heart arises from bilateral rudiments that

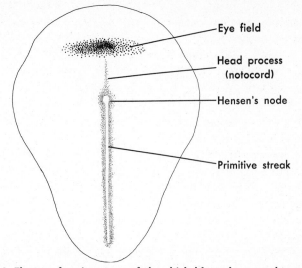

Figure 5·6. The eye-forming area of the chick blastoderm at the stage of the head process. [Adapted from B. H. Willier and M. E. Rawles, in *Proc. Soc. Exptl. Biol. Med.,* 32:1293–1296, 1935.]

subsequently fuse to form a single organ. Within the individual fields, however, heart-forming potency is not evenly distributed, for beating heart tissues form most frequently in grafts taken from near the geometric center of the field, and this frequency falls off progressively toward the periphery of the area. The heart field thus exhibits gradients of heart-forming potentiality.

The eye field has been located at primitive-streak stages in the chick embryo by means of similar grafting experiments. At first, this is a single field with the high point of eye-forming potency in its center— actually, in the region that normally forms the floor of the forebrain (Figure 5·6). As the chick enters the somite-forming stages, the capacity for eye formation gradually increases in right and left sides of the field while diminishing at the center; by the time eight somites have been formed, the medial region of the original field territory has lost the capacity to form eye. This is an instance in which nature subdivides a morphogenetic field as a normal developmental event, each part of the divided field then retaining the capacity to form a whole organ.

Usually, the field properties extend beyond the limits of tissue that actually contribute to the construction of the specific organ. For example, the circumscribed area in the urodele embryo that normally contributes to the formation of a limb or a gill will form that structure when grafted to another location, but material from the wound edge, *in situ,* will now form the organ in the absence of the main part of the field.

Almost all our discussion thus far signals the fact that development is the constant creation of new and diverse structures in increasingly complex relationships. Each developmental process, viewed in any one cross section of time, is going on against the background of what occurred during the preceding period of time; it then sets the stage for what will be done in the next time interval. The total process of the progressive building up of the newer and more diverse from the stuff of the older and more homogeneous is called *epigenesis*.

The epigenetic view of development is in distinct contrast to the older and largely discredited view that realization of the specific form of the organism results simply from the expansion of preexisting diversity in the egg or sperm. Some preformationists of an earlier era seriously conisdered that all parts of the adult are represented in the ovum and need merely to be activated by the sperm and nourished in order to grow to adult size. Such a view, of course, required that the eggs of the adult generation must necessarily contain the eggs of the next, and the next, and the next generation ad infinitum—clearly a ridiculous thesis. Another view had it that there are in the unsegmented egg the preformed "germs" of the various organs, forerunners of the organs themselves.

These ideas now impress us as foolish, but there actually are a number of eggs in which cytoplasmic zones of distinctive appearance become segregated before cleavage begins, and these zones can be traced to particular organs or systems. Eggs of this kind are called *mosaic eggs,* for if such an organ-forming zone is deleted, the structure it would normally have formed is absent in the resulting embryo or larva.

The protochordate *Styela* has eggs of the mosaic type. At fertilization, complicated streaming movements of the oöplasm lead to establishment of as many as four recognizable organ-forming zones. On one side, partly below the equator, there arises a crescentic zone of yellowish protoplasm, rich in mitochondria, that forms the musculature and connective tissue; opposite this crescent is a somewhat grayish zone that forms the neural tube and notochord; at the vegetal pole is a slate-gray, yolky zone that forms the gut; and in the animal half lies the material that forms the ectoderm (Figure 5·7). The egg is thus bilaterally symmetrical even before the first cleavage, and blastomeres that are isolated after cleavage begins and that are allowed to develop form essentially only what they would have formed if left in association with their fellows in the intact egg. Eggs bisected meridionally in the plane of bilateral symmetry just before the first cleavage form right or left half-embryos according to which side receives the nucleus.

Eggs that have a rigid cleavage pattern with predictable fates for individual blastomeres are also said to have *determinate cleavage.*

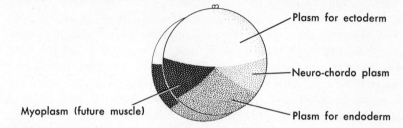

Fig. 5·7. The distribution of organ-forming plasms of the egg of *Styela* at the two-cell stage. The first cleavage divides the egg and its distinctive ctyoplasmic zones into right and left halves. [Adapted from B. I. Balinsky, *An Introduction to Embryology*, 2d ed., Philadelphia: Saunders, 1965, p. 154.]

Eggs of this kind are found among annelids and mollusks that show spiral cleavage. Of particular interest in the present context are those that form a *polar lobe* during the first divisions of the zygote. During the first cleavage, one blastomere pinches off a lobe of protoplasm at its vegetal end. The lobe remains attached to the daughter blastomere by a narrow neck, and once the separation of the cells is completed, the material of the lobe flows back into the blastomere whence it arose, making it much larger than the other one. During the next cleavage, the lobe forms again, and once more it flows back into a daughter cell when division is completed (Figure 5·8). The polar lobe may be severed from the egg during the stage of its greatest size during the first division, the *trefoil* stage, and the two blastomeres allowed to develop without the contributions of the lobe. The resulting larva develops essentially without mesoderm, thus giving the impression that a special plasm is prelocalized in the polar lobe.

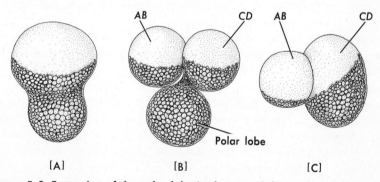

Figure 5·8. Formation of the polar lobe in the egg of the mud snail *Ilyanassa*. A: Protrusion of the polar lobe as the first cleavage begins. **B:** The first cleavage furrow separates blastomeres AB and CD; the polar lobe remains attached to CD. **C:** The polar lobe is assimilated into CD upon completion of the first cleavage. [Adapted from T. H. Morgan, *Experimental Embryology*, New York: Columbia, 1927, p. 360.]

In contrast to the mosaic eggs are those called *regulative eggs*, in which organ-forming plasms are not recognized; these eggs are said to have *indeterminate cleavage*. The sea urchin provides an example of such an egg. In this egg, as we have seen, a half-blastula can regulate to form the whole, and the absence of a blastomere after the first or second cleavage does not prevent normal development; during cleavage stages, two embryos may be fused, with animal-vegetal axes coinciding, to give a single giant larva. We can thus say that the egg of the sea urchin is highly regulative, but we should keep in mind that animal and vegetal zones are nevertheless the sites of considerably different developmental tendencies.

The egg of the amphibian was once thought of as a mosaic egg, but it is actually highly regulative. In the frog, if the first two blastomeres are separated experimentally and if the first cleavage plane has passed through the gray crescent, two normal tadpoles may form. If the gray-crescent material is entirely in one blastomere, however, only the one receiving it will form a larva. Thus there is a prelocalization of material in the amphibian egg that is tied in with the invagination of the chordamesoderm field in later development.

A consideration of such cases as the organ-forming crescents of the protochordate, the gray crescent of the frog or urodele, and the polar lobe of the mollusk indicates that there is some usefulness in invoking to a limited degree a preformationistic view of development, if only to emphasize that an egg, by the time it is ready to cleave, may have a rather pronounced regional organization of its cytoplasm. The difference between mosaic and regulative eggs is the degree to which rigid structuring of organ-forming areas occurs.

But does the apparent preformation of organ-forming areas or centers of particular morphogenetic potencies indicate that certain attributes of egg organization do not arise epigenetically? Actually, what one finds if he examines eggs at sufficiently early stages is that rigidity of developmental pattern simply arises earlier in mosaic eggs than it does in regulative ones. For example, an egg of the protochordate *Ciona* that is bisected by a cut through animal and vegetal poles at the time of first cleavage can form only half-larvae; but an egg similarly cut prior to fertilization can form, upon subsequent insemination, well-formed larvae from either half. This plasticity declines after fertilization and is essentially lost by the time the first cleavage is due. The mosaic condition in this egg is therefore achieved epigenetically.

This emphasis on the epigenetic view notwithstanding, the egg is endowed with a preformed organization in the nucleus. The latter, though clearly not provided with organ-forming substances or preformed organs in miniature, actually does comprise a preformed genetic repertory of coded instructions that determines what structures will eventually be made by the egg and when they will appear. These instructions are the genes on the chromosomes, and they comprise the construction manual for the epigenetic process. How this set of instructions is coded in the nucleus and how the instructions are translated into the epigenetic formation of the embryo will now be our concern.

Genetic Control of Development

WHAT IS ACCOMPLISHED by development, the realization of the phenotype, is determined by the genetic endowment of the zygote. Studies of a generation or more ago in the fields of genetics and cytogenetics give abundant evidence that the genes, the hereditary factors that govern the appearance of specific characteristics, are in the nucleus, where they are arranged in linear fashion on the chromosomes. True, cases of cytoplasmic inheritance have been described, but even in these instances, expression of the cytoplasmically determined characteristics is, in the final analysis, dependent on the action of nuclear genes.

Nuclear Determination of Developmental Events

That the nucleus conveys very specific instructions as to the pattern of morphogenesis is shown by results of nuclear-transplantation experiments. One such experiment was carried out on an alga of the genus *Acetabularia*—not an animal, to be sure, but a plant that has provided all developmental biologists with material whence they have derived excellent insights; it should not be neglected in any analysis of development. This organism is a single cell, but it is regionally differentiated into stalk, rhizoids, and a reproductive cap. The rhizoids anchor the plant to its substratum, and the nucleus resides in one of them at the base of the stalk. At the other end of the stalk is the umbrella-shaped reproductive cap. When the cap is mature, the single nucleus makes numerous daughter nuclei, which migrate to the cap, forming cysts filled with haploid ($1n$) spores. Germination of the cysts releases flagellated swimming cells that fuse in pairs to form the zygote ($2n$), which starts the next generation.

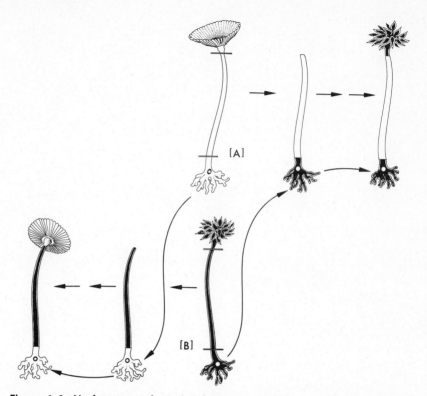

Figure 6·1. Nuclear transplantation between *Acetabularia mediterranea (upper left)* and *A. crenulata (lower right)*. [Adapted from J. Hammerling, in *Zeitschrift für induktive Abstammungs- und Vererbungslehre*, 81:114–180, 1943.]

When a developing cap is severed from the stalk, a new cap regenerates. If the nucleus is removed by severing the rhizoid, no cap can form; but if a new rhizoid is grafted, a cap will develop. Apparently, therefore, the nucelus is required for cap formation. The kind of cap formed varies from species to species. What would be the consequence if nuclei were exchanged between capless stalks of different species? Such an experiment is illustrated in Figure 6·1. When a stalk with severed cap receives a nuclear graft from another species, the regenerating cap shows characteristics intermediate between those of the species represented by stalk and by nucleus. If the cap again be severed, however, the next regenerate shows the form of the species of the nuclear donor, and the stalk continues to produce that kind of cap if repeatedly forced to regenerate one. This indicates that nuclear factors determine the kind of cap formed—in other words, that they determine the pattern of morphogenesis.

This conclusion is further reinforced by cases of nuclear transplantation in multicellular animals. In the Mexican axolotl *Siredon mexicanum* (urodele amphibian), the *white form* of the organism results from a simple recessive mutation (*dd*) that causes the dark melanin pigmentation to be restricted to a narrow band on each side close to the dorsal fin. In the *wild type,* or *dark form* (*DD*), the pigment cells are distributed over most of the body. If one transplants into an activated white egg with functionless nucleus (inactivated by irradiation with ultraviolet light) the diploid nucleus from a cell of the early embryo of a dark animal, the egg develops with a functional dark nucleus and the larva that is formed shows the dark pigmentary pattern characteristic of the nuclear-donor strain (Figure 6·2). Another example is provided by the leopard frog, *Rana pipiens,* in which the *burnsii* mutant shows a diminuation of pigmented spots on the dorsum. In this case, a *burnsii* nucleus transplanted into a nonnucleated (nucleus removed microsurgically) wild-type egg leads to expression of the *burnsii* characteristic in the pigmentary pattern of the resulting frog. Reciprocally, the normal pattern is developed when an enucleate *burnsii* egg develops after receiving a nucleus from a wild-type cell.

These experiments show that the nucleus is the seat of instructions for what is to be made during development. Even though I have emphasized the *morphogenetic* issue of these instructions, it is not difficult to recognize that the instructions must have basically to do with the construction of protein molecules. Protein, after all, is the major structural component of cells: with lipid, it makes the intricate membrane systems of the cellular organelles and cellular boundaries; muscle is largely contractile protein; protein in the form of collagen and elastin binds tissues together; mineralized, it forms bone; with polysaccharide, protein forms much of the intracellular ground substance and the lubricating fluids of the joints. Most fundamentally, for our consideration, protein is the material of which the enzymes are made—the molecules that catalyze the energy-transforming reactions of the cell and the reactions that assemble the building blocks of the cellular materials and extracellular matrices. Truly, the most fundamental aspect of the control of morphogenesis must be the control of the synthesis of the protein catalysts, the enzymes. The kinds and amounts of enzymes and the presence or absence of their substrates determine what energy supplies are available, what building blocks are at hand, and the kinds of structures that will be produced. The distribution of enzymes in time and space thus determines the distribution of synthetic and degradative processes and, ultimately, the form and function of the organism.

That genes bring about a morphogenetic endpoint by direct effects on specific biochemical reactions was first indicated in studies of certain genes that block the appearance of brown pigment in the eye of

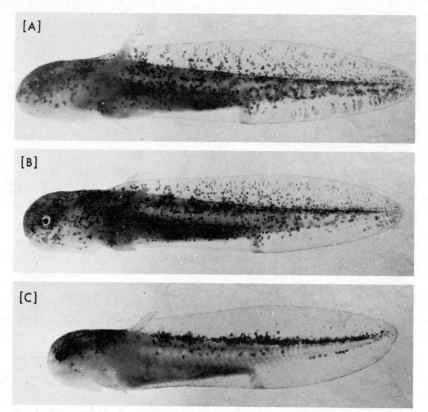

Figure 6·2. Nuclear control of pigmentary pattern in the larva of *Siredon mexicanum*. A: Larva issued from egg of an ultraviolet-irradiated white (*dd*) female injected with the diploid nucleus from the early embryo of a dark, or wild-type, genotype (*DD* or *Dd*). **B:** Control larva of genotype *DD*. **C:** Control larva of genotype *dd*. Note that the *D* gene in *dd* cytoplasm **(A)** duplicates exactly the pigmentary pattern that it shows in its normal environment. [From J. Signoret, R. Briggs, and R. R. Humphrey, in *Developmental Biol.* 4:134–164, 1962. By courtesy of the authors and permission of Academic Press, Inc., New York.]

the fruit fly *Drosophila melanogaster*. The eye contains two kinds of pigments, brown and red. The two pigments are not related and, in the absence of the brown, the eye appears a brilliant red. Four recessive nonallelic genes block the appearance of brown pigment by interfering with its synthesis from the amino acid tryptophane (Figure 6·3). In the vermillion mutant the synthesis of formylkynurenine from tryptophane is blocked, presumably because of a defective or absent enzyme, but if the larva is fed formylkynurenine or if the eye is transplanted to the body of a wild-type host or a nonvermillion mutant in the series, it will make normal brown pigment. Similarly the formation of hydroxykynurenine is blocked by the presence of the cinnabar gene, and steps in the transformation of hydroxykynurenine to brown pigment are blocked by scarlet and cardinal. Subsequently, a more extensive study of biochemical mutants, in the pink bread mold *Neurospora,* revealed dozens of cases in which genetic lesions resulted in failure to form enzymes that were needed to catalyze specific steps in the synthesis of strategic metabolites.

At the present time, it can be readily shown in bacteria and viruses that the genes directly control the synthesis of proteins, even to the extent of specifying the exact sequences of the amino acids that comprise them. This demonstration can likewise be made in higher organisms under some conditions. Thus in gene-controlled sickle-cell anemia of human beings (a disease that affects the shape of the blood cells and their oxygen-carrying capacity), the oxygen-binding pigment hemoglobin is abnormal, for it has the amino acid valine in place of glutamic acid at a certain position in the globin portion of the molecule. A great number of hereditary hemoglobin variants have now been analyzed and found to have differences involving the substitution of only one amino acid.

Apparently, in all organisms the genetic material determines the amino acid sequences of proteins and hence their basic structural and catalytic properties. Development is characterized by changes in the amount, distribution, and diversification of protein, the groundwork for differentiation. Therefore, in order to understand how development is controlled by the genome, one must learn how the nucleus

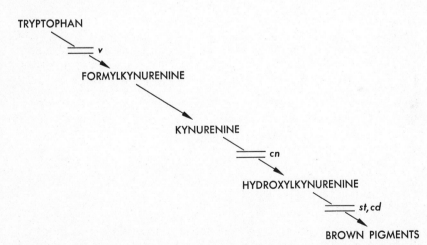

Figure 6·3. Chemical reactions leading to the synthesis of brown pigment in the eye of the fruit fly *Drosophila melanogaster*. Steps in the synthetic pathway may be blocked by certain mutations. v, vermillion; cn, cinnabar; st, scarlet; cd, cardinal. [Adapted from R. P. Wagner and H. K. Mitchell, *Genetics and Metabolism*, New York; Wiley, 1955, p. 215.]

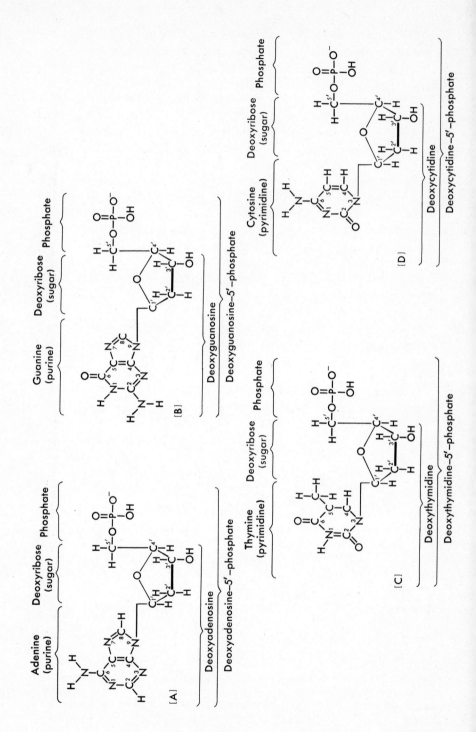

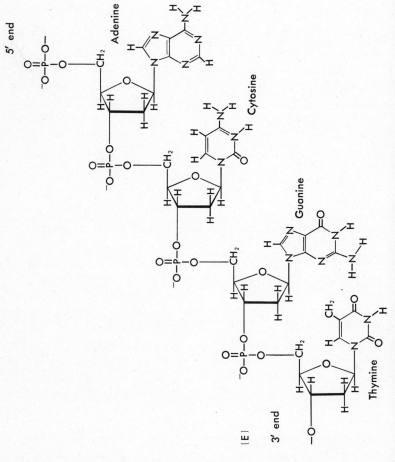

Figure 6·4. The nucleotides of DNA, the nomenclature of their parts, and the way they are linked.

77

determines the orderly sequences of amino acids that comprise the proteins and regulates the kinds and amounts of proteins that are synthesized.

The Genetic Code and How to Translate It

The past decade or so has witnessed a considerable increase in our knowledge of the way genes direct protein synthesis. During this period, our understanding of the control of rates and amounts of synthesis has advanced to a lesser degree. Although insights into these matters have been derived largely from the analysis of protein synthesis in bacteria and viruses, the evidence daily becomes more persuasive that multicellular organisms share with these forms the same basic mechanisms for the control of protein synthesis and hence for the translation of the genotype into the phenotype. We shall consider some of the evidence for this later; first, let us consider the construction manual for development and how its instructions are read out and executed.

DNA

The genes are the construction manual. They are made of *deoxyribose nucleic acids* (DNA), which are high-molecular-weight polymers composed of *nucleotides*. Each nucleotide is formed of a *purine* or *pyrimidine* base, a five-carbon sugar, *deoxyribose* (dR), to which the base is attached, and a *phosphate* group (P) to which the deoxyribose is attached. The nucleotides that form DNA are illustrated in Figure 6·4. Nucleotides can be linked by the formation of an ester bond between the phosphate group of one nucleotide and the 3′-hydroxyl of the deoxyribose moiety of the adjacent one.

The bases found in nucleotides are the purines *adenine* and *guanine* and the pyrimidines *cytosine* and *thymine*. The nucleotides formed with these bases may be united in any linear order to form polynucleotide chains of great length. If we represent each base by its first letter, one such linear array might be that illustrated in Figure 6·5.

Analysis of the bases that are separated out chemically from natural samples of DNA reveals that the amounts of A and T occur in the

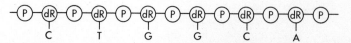

Figure 6·5. A linear array of purine and pyrimidine bases that might occur in a short DNA chain. The bases are represented by their first letters: A, adenine; C, cytosine; G, guanine; T, thymine. The backbone is a chain of alternating moieties of orthophosphate, P, and deoxyribose, dR.

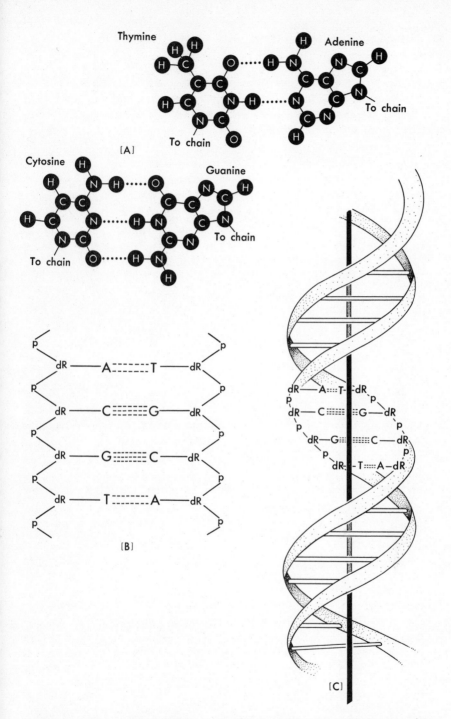

Figure 6·6. The structure of DNA. A: Details of specific base pairing between thymine and adenine, which form two hydrogen bonds, and between guanine and cytosine, which form three hydrogen bonds. **B:** The DNA ladder. **C:** Coiling of the ladder into a helix.

ratio of 1 to 1, and so do the amounts of G and C. The ratios found for $(A + G)/(C + T)$, however, are quite variable. These facts, together with data from x-ray–diffraction studies and the analysis of hydrogen-bonding sites and covalent-bond angles, show that the nucleic acids actually comprise two parallel chains lying side by side in a ladderlike configuration, the sides of the ladder being formed by the dR—P—dR links and the steps being formed by the purine and pyrimidine bases, which project from the sides and are held together by hydrogen bonds. Each step comprises either A and T, held together by three hydrogen bonds, or G and C, held by two of them. Thus in any sample of DNA, A and T always exist in equal numbers, and so do G and C. The entire double-chain molecule is twisted in a helix, so that the ladder is in the form of a spiral stair (Figure 6·6).

Clearly, the sequence of bases on either side of the ladder could comprise a kind of code or a genetic language with an alphabet of four letters. The sequence of bases in DNA is such a code, and the construction manual for development is written in DNA language.

COPYING OF GENES BY RNA

The construction manual is in the nucleus, and the protein, the basis of structure, is mostly synthesized in the cytoplasm of the cell. Obviously, the cytoplasm must have copies of the nuclear instructions and also the means of translating these copies into the amino acid sequences that occur in proteins. These needs are provided for by other kinds of nucleic acids that we lump under the general heading of *ribose nucleic acid,* or RNA. RNA is much like DNA; it is constructed with ribose (R) in place of deoxyribose, however, and it has the pyrimidine uracil (U) in place of thymine (Figure 6·7). Like

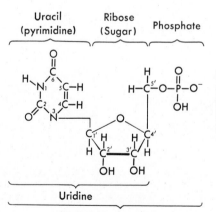

Uracil (pyrimidine)   Ribose (Sugar)   Phosphate

Uridine

Uridine–5′–phosphate

Figure 6·7. The structure of uridine-5′-phosphate. Note the similarity of uracil to thymine. Compare the structure of ribose, shown here, with that of deoxyribose, shown in Figure 6·4.

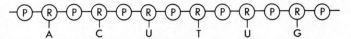

Figure 6·8. A hypothetical RNA chain of ribose (R) and orthophosphate (P), with attached bases. U, uracil; other bases as in Figure 6·5.

DNA, RNA occurs in ribonucleotide chains, but in RNA the bases project from a backbone made up of ribose and phosphate (Figure 6·8).

A glance at this chain shows that the base sequences in RNA, like those of DNA, could also comprise a genetic language written in an alphabet of four letters. This alphabet would be just like that of DNA except for the replacement of thymine (T) by uracil (U), and if one were to make this substitution, he could rewrite or transcribe the code from a single strand of DNA in the form of RNA without changing the genetic words.

One of the forms of RNA that can be extracted from cells seems, indeed, to have the job of copying DNA words having to do with the construction of protein molecules; it is called *messenger RNA* (mRNA) or *template RNA* and it copies only one of the chains of the DNA helix. At the time of copying, the individual RNA nucleotides align themselves, with the aid of the enzyme RNA polymerase,

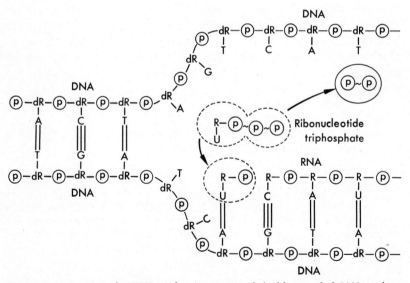

Figure 6·9. Copying the DNA code. A segment of double-stranded DNA is shown opened up, with RNA copying one strand from right to left. At the left is illustrated the attachment of a molecule of uridine phosphate that has been split from uridine triphosphate.

in register with the complementary bases of one strand of the DNA double helix—U of the incipient RNA molecule with A of the DNA; G with C; A with T; C with G (Figure 6·9). Copying of the genetic message occurs in longer or shorter segments of the genome, each describing in genetic language the way a protein molecule or portion thereof should be constructed. The RNA units, of corresponding length, then detach from the DNA helix and move away. Thus it is that items of information about the sequence of amino acids in proteins encoded in the genome are copied.

This information is conveyed by virtue of the arrangement of the four-letter alphabet of RNA into meaningful three-letter words called *codons;* each codon denotes a particular amino acid. Does this provide a sufficiently large vocabulary for the construction manual? Yes, for if one arranges four letters in all possible sequences, three at a time, a total of sixty-four codons is possible (Table 6·1). Since there are only twenty amino acids used in the construction of natural proteins, this vocabulary is clearly adequate. Actually, there are sufficient three-letter groups for superfluous, or degenerate, words, permitting the coding for the same amino acid by more than one group. Nucleotide sequences coding for the various amino acids are shown in Table 6·2.

TRANSLATION OF THE GENETIC MESSAGE BY RNA

Given a vocabulary that has a word for each amino acid, the structure of a protein might be called for in the RNA language by a finite number of codons linearly arranged in the same order as the amino acids that comprise the protein to be manufactured. There would next be required a mechanism for translating the RNA codons into the specific amino acids represented by each. This requirement is met in the cell by another kind of RNA, of relatively low molecular weight, called *soluble RNA* (sRNA).[1]

For each kind of amino acid used in the building of protein, there is transcribed from the genome at least one specific kind of soluble RNA, comprising a distinctive chain of about eighty ribonucleotides. Such chains are alike in the sense of having the same terminal bases— cytosine, cytosine, and adenine, in that order—and in having guanine as the first base at the other end of the chain. Base sequences in the intervening portions of the chain differ for each kind of sRNA; They are being worked out in detail for a number of sRNAs at the time of writing (Figure 6·10). Some of the purine and pyrimidine bases of the

---

[1] Soluble RNA is so called because it remains soluble in 1 *M* NaCl, which precipitates other RNAs. It is often referred to as *transfer RNA*.

TABLE 6·1
Possible Codons for mRNA

AAA	AAG	AAC	AAU
AGA	AGG	AGC	AGU
ACA	ACG	ACC	ACU
AUA	AUG	AUC	AUU
GAA	GAG	GAC	GAU
GGA	GGG	GGC	GGU
GCA	GCG	GCC	GCU
GUA	GUG	GUC	GUU
CAA	CAG	CAC	CAU
CGA	CGG	CGC	CGU
CCA	CCG	CCC	CCU
CUA	CUG	CUC	CUU
UAA	UAG	UAC	UAU
UGA	UGG	UGC	UGU
UCA	UCG	UCC	UCU
UUA	UUG	UUC	UUU

TABLE 6·2
Amino Acid Code Words: The Genetic Code

Amino Acid	Codons					
Alanine	GCU	GCC	GCA	GCG		
Arginine	CGU	CGC	CGA	CGG	AGA	AGG
Asparagine	AAU	AAC				
Aspartic acid	GAU	GAC				
Cysteine	UGU	UGC				
Glutamic acid	GAA	GAG				
Glutamine	CAA	CAG				
Glycine	GGU	GGC	GGA	GGG		
Histidine	CAU	CAC				
Isoleucine	AUU	AUC	AUA			
Leucine	UUA	UUG	CUU	CUC	CUA	CUG
Lysine	AAA	AAG				
Methionine	AUG					
Phenylalanine	UUU	UUC				
Proline	CCU	CCC	CCA	CCG		
Serine	AGU	AGC				
Threonine	ACU	ACC	ACA	ACG		
Tryptophan	UGG					
Tyrosine	UAU	UAC				
Valine	GUU	GUC	GUA	GUG		

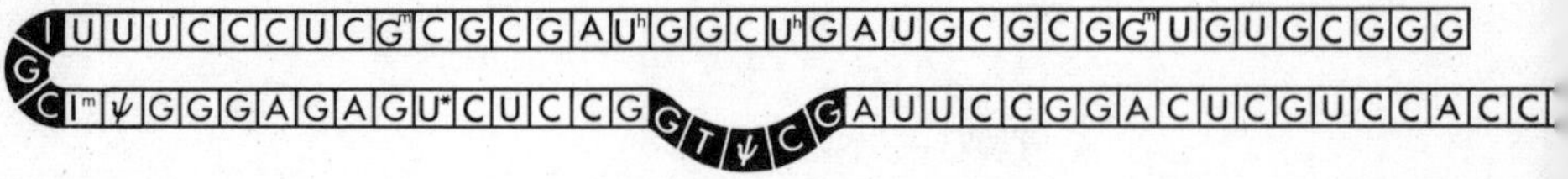

I U U U C C U C G' C G C G A U' G G C U' G A U G C G C G G' U G U G C G G G
G C I^m ψ G G G A G A G U' C U C C G — G T ψ C — G A U U C C G G A C U C G U C C A C C

Figure 6·10. The sequence of bases in the sRNA that is specific to the amino acid alanine. No attempt is made to depict the three-dimensional structure of the molecule, which was not completely resolved at the time of writing. The terminal sequence of bases, —CCA, is common to all sRNAs, the transported amino acid being linked by covalent bond to the ribose of adenylic acid (see Figure 6·11). The sequence ICG probably matches with the code word for alanine, which is GCG. (I, inosine, is similar in structure to cytosine and forms three hydrogen bonds with guanine, as does cytosine.) The series of bases GTψCG may be the sequence that binds the sRNA molecule to the ribosome (see Figure 6·12). The symbol ψ denotes pseudouridine, a compound similar to uridine, but with atoms N and C at position 3 and 5 interchanged.

sRNA molecules are methylated and otherwise slightly modified, and all sRNAs are thought to contain a special sequence comprising guanine, thymine, pseudouridine, cytosine, and guanine in that order (note that appropriate methylation of uracil gives thymine; see Figures 6·4 and 6·7). The three-dimensional structures of the sRNAs are also being analyzed, and it appears that there is folding and cross linking with some helical structure. Each kind of sRNA is thought to have a fold in the nucleotide chain, exposing a sequence of bases complementary to bases in the messenger RNA codon of the amino acid for which it is specific. This sequence is called an *anticodon*.

Each kind of sRNA has the task of transporting the specific amino acid for which it has the anticodon to an assembly site where the amino acid will be joined with others in the sequence prescribed by the mRNA for a particular protein. This assembly site is provided by a special organelle, the *ribosome,* and the special five-base sequence noted above possibly serves in binding the sRNA to the ribosome.

Before describing the ribosomes and the assembly process, however, it is appropriate to examine the attachment of the amino acid to its sRNA (Figure 6·11) and to take cognizance of the remarkable group of enzymes that facilitate this attachment. For each kind of amino acid–sRNA pair there is a special enzyme called *activating enzyme* or *amino acyl synthetase.* Each activating enzyme has two reactive sites, one for binding its amino acid and another for adapting to the specific sRNA for that acid. The enzyme activates the amino acid by catalyzing its reaction with *adenosine triphosphate* (ATP), the high-energy compound generated principally in oxidative metabolism. This results in the release of pyrophosphate (P ~ P) from ATP and the formation of a high-energy covalent bond between *adenosine monophosphate* (AMP) and the activated amino acid. The resulting molecule, AA ~ AMP, remains bound to the enzyme (E)

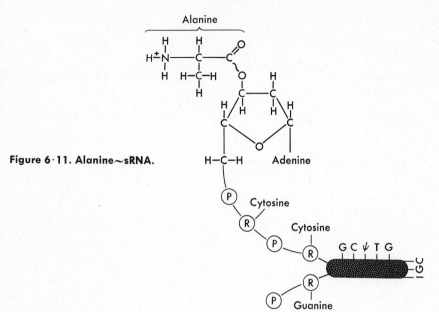

Figure 6·11. Alanine~sRNA.

$$AA + ATP + E \rightarrow AA \sim AMP\text{---}E + P \sim P$$

until there is an effective collision with the appropriate sRNA molecule. The enzyme thereupon binds by its reactive site to the sRNA and then catalyzes the formation of a covalent bond between the amino acid and the ribose of the terminal adenylic nucleotide of the sRNA. AMP is thereupon released, and the activating enzyme detaches, free to activate and transport another molecule of the same amino acid.

$$AA \sim AMP\text{---}E + sRNA \rightarrow AA \sim sRNA + AMP + E$$

The sRNA then unloads its amino acid at the ribosome.

RIBOSOMES, THE SITES OF PROTEIN SYNTHESIS

The ribosome, as its name indicates, contains RNA. This RNA, conveniently called rRNA, is transcribed from a small portion of the genome and is then combined with protein to form a ribosome. This structure binds for reaction both the mRNA (a sequence of codons) and sRNA, with anticodons and the amino acids specified by the codons. Each ribosome comprises two subunits, one with a molecular weight of about 500,000 and the other about twice that size. At present, it is thought that the smaller subunit provides a site for the attachment of mRNA and that the larger has sites for binding

AA ~ sRNAs (Figure 6·12). The two subunits are presumably held together in such a way that the codon sequences of the mRNA are at the boundaries of the sites that bind AA ~ sRNA.

Protein synthesis begins with the attachment of one end of the mRNA to the ribosome and the insertion of an AA ~ sRNA into the larger subunit at the site bounded by the first codon of the mRNA. This site could conceivably accept any AA ~ sRNA, but it accepts the one that carries the appropriate anticodon for the first mRNA codon and the particular amino acid called for by that codon.[2] After the first AA ~ sRNA is attached, a second one affixes to an adjacent binding site on the larger ribosomal subunit. The amino acid carried by this next AA ~ sRNA is the one that is specified by the second codon of the mRNA molecule. With the second amino acid present, a peptide bond is formed between it and the first one. The sRNA for the first is now released from its binding site and diffuses away. The second AA ~ sRNA now moves into the site vacated by the first, carrying with it the linked amino acids. The mRNA next shifts the third codon of its sequence into place on the ribosome, and this specifies a third AA ~ sRNA, which will move into the place just vacated by the second. Peptide bonds then unite the second and third amino acids, the mRNA moves its next codon into place, another amino acid is added, and so on until the entire protein molecule, as written out in the sequence of mRNA codons, is translated into a chain of amino acids. The terminal amino acid of the protein is released from the last sRNA, and the sRNA is released from the ribosome. The ribosome is then available for combination with another molecule of mRNA, and the sRNA is free to combine with another molecule of its specific amino acid.

Molecules of mRNA are often relatively lengthy, and because the part of the molecule in contact with a single ribosome is relatively short, a single message can move through the binding sites of several ribosomes in succession, thus creating a chain of ribosomes held together by the mRNA strand. Depending on the length of the messenger molecule, varying numbers of ribosomes may be moving in succession along it. The messenger for one of the polypeptide chains of hemoglobin, for example, is about 1,500 angstrom units (Å) in length. This could accommodate comfortably five or six ribosomes, each with a diameter of 230 Å. The messenger for the enzyme beta galactosidase could have as many as forty ribosomes strung along its length. When ribosomes of cells engaged in active protein synthesis are

---

[2] At this writing, there is some evidence suggesting that there may be a special codon-anticodon pair that is necessary to initiate the binding process in the synthesis of all proteins.

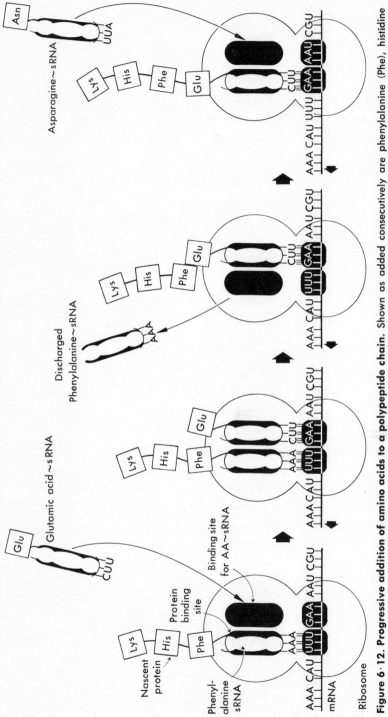

Figure 6·12. Progressive addition of amino acids to a polypeptide chain. Shown as added consecutively are phenylalanine (Phe), histidine (His), lysine (Lys), glutamic acid (Glu), and, at the right, asparagine (Asn). [Adapted from J. D. Watson, *Molecular Biology of the Gene*. New York: W. A. Benjamin, Inc., 1965 p. 336.]

87

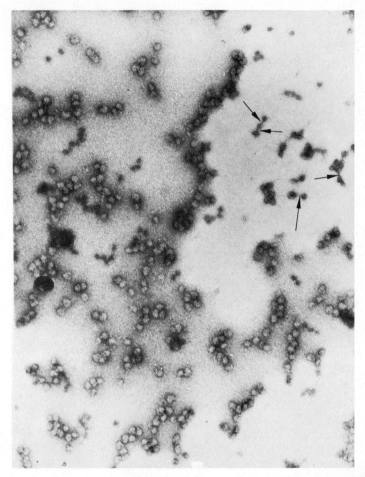

**Figure 6·13. Electron micrograph of polyribosomes isolated from the unferti-
lized egg of the surf clam *Spisula*.** The individual ribosomes in the clusters are possibly connected to the neighbors on either side by strands of mRNA (arrows) but
in this particular case presence of the mRNA has not been proved. [From E. Bell
and R. Reeder in *Biochim. et. Biophys. Acta*, 142:500–511, 1967. By courtesy of
Dr. Bell and Elsevier Publishing Co.]

separated gently from other cellular components and placed on a
carbon-coated grid for electron microscopy, they form clusters in
which the individual ribosomes are apparently held in linear array by
mRNA (Figure 6·13). In electron micrographs of sectioned cells, the
clusters are often quite evident but the connecting mRNA strand is
not easily seen. These clusters are sometimes called *polysomes* or *polyribosomes*.

I have now presented the basic outline of the mechanism whereby
proteins are synthesized in accordance with instructions coded in the

nucleus. In sum: A segment of the genome coding for a particular protein is read out, or transcribed, in the form of messenger RNA. The message then feeds its codons sequentially through ribosomal binding sites; as it does so, soluble RNAs translate the message, discharging their amino acids in the order called for by the sequence of codons in the mRNA; peptide bonds form between successive amino acids; and when the sequence is assembled, the finished protein is released from the ribosome.

Control of Genetic Readout during Development: Today's Challenge

We recognize that a fundamental accomplishment of embryonic development in higher organisms is the differentiation of discontinuous cellular types (see Chapter 5). The distinctiveness of a kind of cell has its basis in its differential patterns of synthetic activities; muscle cells make actin and myosin, reticulocytes produce hemoglobin, fibroblasts synthesize collagen, and so on. But cells otherwise quite different from one another engage in many of the same kinds of syntheses: those that comprise dividing populations of whatever kind, for example, must make spindle proteins and certain kinases and polymerases that are catalytically active in replication of chromosomes; and all cells, whether dividing or not, must maintain appropriate kinds and quantities of enzymes for catalyzing the reactions in their normal cycles of energy generation and expenditure. In other words, each kind of cell must transcribe and translate messages appropriate to its need for the catalytic and structural proteins used in executing the special functions of its differentiated state and also the proteins appropriate to producing the materials essential to its normal housekeeping duties.

These considerations indicate that during development it must be established for each kind of cell what portions of its genome are to be used in executing its definitive developmental assignment. These considerations also lead us to realize that mechanisms for controlling the reading and translation of the genome are operating at each stage of development. These mechanisms determine what gene-directed syntheses are to go on, when, and in what cells and tissues; and they control the rates at which the synthetic products are assembled and degraded. It is the task of the modern developmental biologist to elucidate the nature of these controls.

A COMPLETE CONSTRUCTION MANUAL IN ALL CELLS

Does each cell possess during development a complete set of genetic instructions? In other words, is the entire genome present in each cell regardless of its functional assignment? This seems to be so, at least during early stages, for under experimental conditions embryonic cells can carry out far more extensive developmental assignments than they are normally called upon to execute. As already noted, a half-blastula of the sea urchin can make both right and left sides of a normal larva. When a urodele egg is constricted so that the nucleus is isolated on one side of the constriction, the nucleated side divides to form many cells; if the constriction is then eased slightly so that a late cleavage nucleus can cross the cytoplasmic bridge to the nonnucleated side, it will there divide, and ultimately a complete larva will form from that side of the egg as well as from the other.

Another insight into this question is provided by results of nuclear-transplantation experiments. In the leopard frog, *Rana pipiens,* isolated nuclei from blastulae, gastrulae, and even from neurulae have been implanted into activated, enucleated eggs and have fostered there the development of normal swimming tadpoles. With increasing frequency as development proceeds, however, donor nuclei become less able to bring about normal embryogenesis, and there occur, indeed, rather different patterns of abnormal development that may be correlated with the regional origin of the donor nucleus. The African clawed toad *Xenopus* has been the subject of similar experiments, but one finds in this form that nuclei from cells of the intestinal epithelium of the swimming tadpole may serve, although with rather low frequency, to promote normal development of enucleated, activated eggs. These few cells, at least, must be considered to possess the complete blueprint for development, and it seems probable that most cells do, even during advanced stages, there being differences from stage to stage, species to species, and tissue to tissue in the degree to which the genome can be exposed for reading. Even at late stages, however, many tissues show the ability to undertake synthesis of a new spectrum of proteins for which hitherto unused or little-used sets of instructions must be read. We have noted, for example, that removal of the lens of the eye of the urodele in larval or adult life is followed by regeneration of a new lens from the dorsal margin of the iris. This process requires the abundant synthesis of *crystallins,* specific lens proteins that were not being synthesized in appreciable quantities in the iris cells before their transformation.

CONTROL OF PROTEIN SYNTHESIS DURING DEVELOPMENT

It appears, then, that all nucleated cells do have the complete set of genetic instructions. There remains the very difficult problem of learning the mechanisms that specify for each kind of cell what portion of the genome it can read out and translate, what it is that determines the time, rate, and quantity of transcription, and the rate and amount of translation that occurs. From the preceding discussion it will be recognized that those kinds of proteins that a cell *can* synthesize are determined by the coding sequences of DNA that can be transcribed. For the most part, we do not know the developmental processes that determine that some sites shall be covered or otherwise prevented from being transcribed in an essentially irreversible manner and, conversely, that others will be reversibly masked. The histone proteins, prominently associated with nuclei, have been implicated in the role of masking agent, for some investigators have reported that addition of histones to systems in which DNA is being used to code RNA transcription diminishes the synthesis of RNA. But in some tissues, chromosomal sites of temporarily stimulated RNA synthesis have been shown to have no less histone than other sites that are apparently not being transcribed. The synthesis of messenger RNA on the DNA template requires that the enzyme RNA polymerase have access to the helical DNA templates. Clearly, any configuration of the chromatin that blocks access of the enzyme to the DNA will prevent transcription. Thus readout does not occur when the chromosomes are coiled for mitosis and meiosis nor does it occur in the heterochromatic regions of interphase chromosomes. It is unlikely, too, that new synthesis of RNA occurs during the period when the chromosome is replicating preparatory to the next mitosis.

Of course, even when a segment of the genome is available—that is, exposed to transcription—the occurrence of protein synthesis, its rate, and its quantity are subject to control at other sites. It almost goes without saying that the availability of energy sources and substrates for forming messenger RNA and for the components of the translation system—sRNA, ribosomes, amino acids, and the appropriate enzymes —is of prime consideration. To carry out the instructions of the genome, there must be the building blocks and molds and there must be the power to assemble the parts. But granted these basic characteristics of the system, a number of aspects of the translation process may exercise a predominant influence on *what* is made during development and *when*.

IMPORTANCE OF PERSISTING MESSAGE.   In microorganisms, where the messenger hypothesis first found application, mRNA is generally degraded very soon after its synthesis. So in order for a specific protein to be produced in quantity, the appropriate segment of the genome must be transcribed with some frequency; otherwise the translating system would possibly lack copies to follow. Rapid degradation of messages might be of some advantage to a bacterium, for it is subjected to rapidly changing conditions in nature that might require the reading out of a different portion of the genome and the subsequent switching on of a new synthesis under circumstances wherein a prior synthesis is of no use. The new message being transcribed might then be translated, unhampered by competition with obsolete messages for energy, sRNA, and ribosomes.

For higher organisms, however, normal development often leads to a condition in which cells engage for prolonged periods, or even indefinitely, in the synthesis of a relatively few proteins peculiar to their differentiated state. For these cells, there would be advantage in having messengers that persist for long periods—have a long *half-life*—and so can be translated over and over again. Energy would thus not be expended in frequent transcribing of the genome, and synthesis of protein could go on even under circumstances wherein genetic transcription would be impossible. The latter is, indeed, the case in mammalian reticulocytes. The *reticulocyte,* or *proerythrocyte,* is the stage in the formation of the red blood cell in which the nucleus has just been expelled. In this cell, obviously, there can no longer be transcription of nuclear DNA. Nevertheless, hemoglobin synthesis continues for a prolonged period, as is shown by the incorporation into newly synthesized protein of radioactively labeled amino acids supplied to the reticulocytes. Also, the electron microscope reveals in reticulocytes the presence of characteristic polyribosomes presumably held together by the mRNA that is being translated into the globin moiety of the hemoglobin molecule.

Most embryonic cells, of course, are nucleated, and it would be difficult to determine whether long-lived messengers are present in them were it not for the fact that there is available a drug, actinomycin D, that prevents transcription. It apparently does so by binding to the base, guanine, in the DNA double helix, thus blocking the action of RNA polymerase. In cells treated with appropriate concentrations of this drug, the synthesis of RNA is brought effectively to a standstill, as shown by the fact that they do not incorporate into RNA radioactive uridine supplied to them. In cells so inhibited, the synthesis of protein (as determined by the incorporation of exogenously supplied radioactive amino acids) continues for shorter or longer periods depending on the stability of messenger already present at the time RNA synthesis was cut off. For bacterial cells, this is for only a very few minutes. In HeLa cells (a well-known strain of human cells that has been growing in artificial culture for many years), half the messenger has decayed about three hours after treatment.

For embryonic development, it is tempting to make the generalization that the achievement of a state of stable differentiation in a cell line should be marked by the establishment of a pattern of relatively stable mRNA molecules. This would seem especially reasonable if the major activity of the cell were the manufacture of one or a few spe-

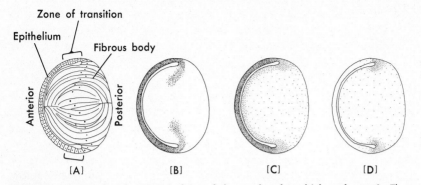

Figure 6·14. Long-lived mRNA in lens of the twelve-day chick embryo. A: The normal lens; cells multiplying in the epithelial layer migrate into and contribute the fibrous body. **B to D:** The pattern of incorporation of radioactivity by isolated lenses incubated in labeled media. **B:** The pattern of incorporation of labeled uridine into RNA during three hours of exposure; label is restricted to cells of the epithelium and to those that have just entered the fibrous body. **C:** The incorporation of radioactive leucine in a lens exposed for one hour to the amino acid; uptake is greatest in the epithelium and that portion of the fibrous body subjacent to it. **D:** The distribution of radioactivity in a lens similarly exposed to labeled leucine but after eight hours of pretreatment with actinomycin D, which presumably prevents RNA transcription. Note that incorporation of leucine continues in the central zone of the fibrous body, just as in the controls, but fails to occur elsewhere; it is most intense at the point where cells are just entering the fibrous body. [Adapted from R. Reeder and E. Bell, in *Science*, 150:71–72, 1965.]

cific products, e.g., myosin, collagen, lens proteins. This has been examined in the lens of the eye in the chick embryo. The lens comprises an anterior epithelial layer and a fibrous body. Cell division occurs chiefly in a band of the epithelium near the equator, cells thence moving into the body of the lens and becoming fibrous (Figure 6·14). When the twelve-day embryonic lens is isolated in vitro in media containing the appropriate radioactive isotopes, the epithelium rapidly incorporates both uridine and amino acids, thus indicating that syntheses of both RNA (presumably including mRNA) and protein are occurring. These syntheses fail to occur, however, in lenses previously exposed to actinomycin D for eight hours. In the fibrous body, there is no incorporation of radioactive uridine regardless of the presence of actinomycin D, but radioactive amino acids are taken up with undiminished speed after the drug treatment. Presumably, therefore, the RNA messages are shorter-lived in cells of the epithelium than in the fibrous body. Possibly, as cells move through the transitional zone into the fibrous core, either their mRNA, which was formerly unstable, is stabilized, or new and stable messages are transcribed from a different part of the genome.

DEFERRAL OF TRANSLATING THE MESSAGE.   There are a number

of systems in which it appears that protein synthesis is controlled by mechanisms that initiate the translation of a message previously synthesized but hitherto unused. The best-known example of this kind of control is found in phenomena associated with fertilization. When the freshly shed unfertilized egg of the sea urchin is exposed to radioactive amino acids, it shows very little incorporation of the radioactivity into protein. Upon fertilization or parthenogenetic activation, however, amino acid uptake into protein increases dramatically. Homogenates of unfertilized and fertilized (or artificially activated) eggs show corresponding effects: preparations from the latter, but not the former, rapidly incorporate amino acids into proteins. The results with intact eggs, therefore, cannot be attributed to effects of fertilization on the permeability of the egg-cell membrane to amino acids.

When, however, homogenates of unfertilized or fertilized eggs are supplied synthetic messenger RNA (e.g., polyuridilic acid, or poly U, a chain of repeating units of uridilic acid that codes for the amino acid phenylalanine; see Table 6·2), there is rapid incorporation of phenylalanine. At first glance, therefore, it would appear that little protein synthesis occurs in unfertilized eggs because mRNA is unavailable; fertilization would presumably initiate transcription of mRNA having to do with the synthesis of protein needed for cleavage and other activities associated with early developmental stages. This being so, one would expect that unfertilized eggs deprived of their nuclei and then exposed to radioactive amino acids and activated would fail to show enhanced incorporation. Such has proved *not* to be the case. Nonnucleated halves of unfertilized sea-urchin eggs (produced by centrifugal force) show an increased incorporation of amino acids into protein in an essentially normal manner immediately upon fertilization or artificial activation.

These results suggest quite strongly that mRNA is present in the cytoplasm of the unfertilized egg in a masked or inactive form. It would have been synthesized, presumably, during oöcyte stages, but we do not know with any certainty where and how it was stored in the interim.

AVAILABILITY OF COMPONENTS OF THE TRANSLATING SYSTEM. As we have seen, the ribosomes of the unfertilized sea-urchin egg are quite capable of interacting with mRNA and of serving as sites for the translation of its message. Thus when an artificial message of polyuridilic acid is supplied, phenylalanine is incorporated rapidly at a time when the normal message is being protected from translation. But even when message is available to functional ribosomes, other components of the translating apparatus could conceivably limit the synthesis of protein. Suppose there were only a few molecules of sRNA; or suppose that the supply of activating enzymes for adapting the amino acids to sRNA were in short supply. Actually, only a few investigations have been directed to issues of these kinds, and it is not clear how widespread might be control mechanisms operating on these components of the translating system. In the unfertilized sea-urchin egg, it appears that the supply of active sRNA is rather low in comparison with the amounts of activating enzymes. This was learned from experiments in which homogenates of unfertilized eggs were examined for protein synthesis in the presence of synthetic poly U, with and without added sRNA prepared from yeast. With the extraneous sRNA, incorporation of phenylalanine into protein was increased many times. Thus with the normal ribosomal population and an appropriate ration of message, translation of poly U into polyphenylalanine is dependent, in this system, on the amount of sRNA. Obviously, activating enzyme for phenylalanine is in plentiful supply or no amino acid above the control amount could be brought to the ribosomes.

The situation I have just outlined is, of course, a highly artificial one. Nature itself has provided a rather dramatic example of translation control, one in which the supply of new ribosomes at a critical stage of development is possibly a limiting factor to protein synthesis and hence to survival of the organism. The preponderance of evidence now indicates that the nucleolus is the site for the synthesis of ribosomal RNA and that it is synthesized by transcription of a very limited portion of the genome. Special regions of the chromosomes serve as nucleolar-organizing centers, often distinguished as visible constrictions of metaphase chromosomes. In the toad *Xenopus*, there is normally a nucleolar-organizing center in each haploid set of chromosomes. Thus in the diploid wild-type individual there are two nucleoli, one organized at the center in each set of chromosomes. A mutation has been found, however, in which the nucleolar organizer is lacking. Heterozygotes show only one nucleolus and are quite viable; homozygous mutants have no nucleolus and die shortly after the tail-bud stage. When the one-nucleolate (1-nu) heterozygotes are mated, the offspring constitute 2-nu, 1-nu, and 0-nu individuals in the proportion of 1 to 2 to 1. The defect of the nucleolar organizer is thus inherited as a simple Mendelian recessive trait.

In *Xenopus*, as in some other kinds of embryos that have been carefully studied, development prior to gastrulation normally proceeds with the aid of *old* ribosomes, i.e., ribosomes synthesized during oögenesis. Only after gastrulation does any *new* ribosomal synthesis become detectable, and at this time the nucleoli make their first appearance. In *Xenopus*, a few new ribosomes appear in the cytoplasm before the tail-bud stage, and shortly thereafter, there is a considerable increase in protein synthesis. But anucleolate (0-nu) mutant embryos do not make new ribosomes, do not increase their protein synthesis, and die. It seems rather likely that there is a causal connection between failure of new ribosomal synthesis and failure of survival.

On the other hand, the ribosomal RNA manufactured in the oöcyte does persist in the mutant embryos, and they develop to the swimming stage before dying. Clearly, as the number of cells increases and as there are increasing demands for synthesis of more proteins, the old ribosomes would be expected to be insufficient to meet the requirements for rapid translation. But does failure occur at the swimming stage in the 0-nu embryos simply because there are too few ribosomes, because the old ones are worn out, or because there is a need for new ones made in the embryonic, rather than maternal environment? This question is not clearly answered as yet, but it is likely that it soon will be.

DETERMINATION BY EXTRINSIC FACTORS OF WHAT PART OF THE GENOME WILL BE TRANSCRIBED DURING DEVELOPMENT.   As we have seen, the nucleus of an advanced amphibian embryo, or even of a swimming tadpole, can serve as the genetic guide for development of an entire organism when it is placed in the cytoplasmic environment of an activated, enucleated egg. Presumably, it does so because the environment of the oöplasm causes the older nucleus to revert to the readout pattern and translation sequence characteristic of the newly formed zygote nucleus. This is a reasonable view, for evidence is rapidly accumulating that transcription of specific segments of the genome can be elicited by altering particular aspects of the environment in which the readout occurs.

We have noted that in normal development of *Xenopus* new ribosomes are not synthesized until after gastrulation and that they first accumulate in the nucleoli. Clearly, the sites of ribosomal readout are repressed during the early stages and are derepressed at gastrulation. (The terms *repression* and *derepression* were introduced in connection with the control of protein synthesis in microorganisms, and they are increasingly used in application to studies of other organisms; they have somewhat specific connotations but are used here in the same general sense as "masked" and "unmasked," or "protected" and "unprotected.") We may now ask what the behavior of the nucleolus is when the nucleus from an advanced *Xenopus* embryo or larva is placed in the cytoplasm of the uncleaved, activated egg. Does ribosomal transcription continue, or does that segment of the genome where the ribosomal sequence is encoded become repressed? Careful studies have shown that the latter is the case. After a few minutes of residence in the host cytoplasm, the introduced nucleus ceases completely the synthesis of ribosomal RNA and the nucleoli imported with it disappear, not to be reorganized until after gastrulation. Apparently, factors of the cytoplasmic environment determine whether transcription of the portions of the genome that code for rRNA is to occur.

Genetic sites for coding specific protein syntheses are likewise under the control of factors of the environment in which the genome operates. Thus in the freshly isolated retina of the chick embryo, the enzyme glutamine synthetase shows little or no activity until about the seventeenth day of incubation, when functional maturation of the retina occurs. Then activity of the enzyme increases dramatically. If, however, fragments of retina are isolated in organ culture at earlier stages, precocious appearance and very rapid increase of glutamine synthetase occur, even in the absence of comparably accelerated histological differentiation. Other kinds of tissues do not respond in this way, but the neural retina does so, even when cultured under conditions that are less than optimal for growth and differentiation. This seems to be a case in which environmental factors elicit readout of a specific portion of the genome, for the precocious rise in the activity of glutamine synthetase is prevented by treatment of the cultures with actinomycin D, which, as already noted, prevents the copying of the DNA code into messenger RNA. The drug puromycin, which inhibits translation, is likewise effective in preventing the increase in activity of the enzyme when neural retina is put in culture.

The factors of the environment that release the transcription of a particular message or its translation into protein can sometimes be identified. For glutamine synthetase, the effective agent seems to be a steroid hormone in the blood serum used in preparing the culture medium, but the exact mechanism whereby it produces its effect is not yet known. In many other tissue-culture situations, manipulation of the milieu affects the synthetic patterns of the treated cells. When a collagen substratum is provided to embryonic chick skeletal-muscle cells plated out on a plastic dish, they synthesize contractile proteins; without the collagen, they simply assume the indifferent, or fibroblastic, configuration (Figure 6·15). When embryonic cartilage cells are separated from their matrices and grown as single layers of cells in tissue-culture vessels, they assume a flattened, stellate shape, undergo fairly rapid cell division, and fail to synthesize chondroitin sulfate, a characteristic component of cartilage. Harvested from the glass surface and centrifuged into compact pellets, these same cells cease mitotic division and commence the synthesis of cartilage material. For these and numerous other cases, we recognize that the onset of particular synthetic patterns (and the turnoff of others—proteins for the mitotic spindle, for example) is determined by factors that emerge or become controlling when a critical mass of cells is brought together or when an association of particular cell types occurs. By and large, what these

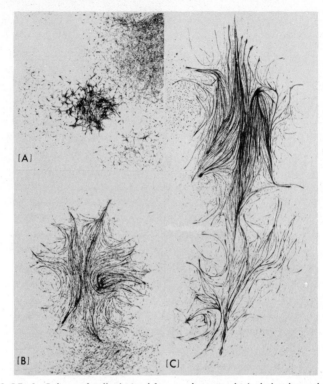

Figure 6·15. A: Colony of cells derived from embryonic chick skeletal muscle growing on a plastic surface; most cells show the stellate configuration characteristic of fibroblasts. **B:** Similar colony on plastic, growing in medium conditioned by prior incubation with freshly dissociated cells from embryonic chick skeletal muscle; the long strands are contractile muscle fibers, or myotubes, formed by the confluence of many myoblasts. **C:** Large array of contractile myotubes formed by cells of embryonic chick skeletal muscle growing in unconditioned medium but on a plastic surface coated with collagen. [Photographs supplied by Dr. I. R. Konigsberg.]

factors are and exactly where they act on the protein-synthetic process are not known.

In a number of instances, the reading of some segments of the genome apparently can be controlled more or less directly by hormones. Some enzymes of liver—tryptophane pyrollase, tyrosine transaminase, glutamic-alanine transaminase, to name some of them—are shown to be synthesized more rapidly following administration of the adrenal cortical hormone hydrocortisone. The increased synthesis of enzyme is preceded by synthesis of new RNA and is abolished by actinomycin D. Thus, possibly, the hormone promotes formation of mRNA that is then translated into protein. But whether the hormone acts directly on a segment of the genome coding for the enzyme or produces its effect indirectly is still uncertain.

Action of a hormone directly on the genetic material has been suggested for cells of the larval salivary glands in insects of the order Diptera. These cells are very large and have gigantic chromosomes (Figure 6·16). The large size of the chromosomes issues from three factors. First, the homologous chromosomes of each cell are permanently paired (we are accustomed to thinking of pairing only in connection with meiosis; see Chapter 2). Second, they are uncoiled over most of their length, so that each stretches out as a strand many times the metaphase length. Third, each strand is present in multiple copies (they are referred to as *polytene,* or many-stranded). At irregular but frequent intervals along each chromosomal strand, there are regions that remain somewhat coiled, or condensed, and these appear as darkly staining areas. The condensed areas of the replicate strands are in register, so that a pattern of transverse bands is created across the polytene structures. The bands are of such constant and characteristic pattern that each has been given a coded designation for its precise location on its chromosome.

Some bands show elaborate structural changes under certain physiological conditions. The altered regions are called *puffs* and are enlargements of the particular band region. Larger puffs are known as *Balbiani rings.* All puffs, regardless of size, apparently result from the uncoiling of the condensed chromatin strands that constitute the bands, the strands then being thrown out as loops from the main body of the chromosome.

Certain puffs appear in regular sequence at the end of the larval period under the influence of the growth and molting hormone ecdysone, and they appear in characteristic sequence. In the fly *Chironomus tendans,* bands I-18-C and IV-2-B appear within one hour after the injection of ecdysone into the larva, band I-8-A is seen after about five hours, and bands II-14-A and III-9-B are seen only after the lapse of three or four days. These puffs are the sites of rapid incorporation of uridine into RNA, as shown by exposing the glands to radioactive uridine after ecdyosne treatment. Nonpuffing regions take up little or none of the uridine. The onset of puffing and the incorporation of uridine is abolished by treatment of the larva with actinomycin D. Cycloheximide, a drug that inhibits translation but not transcription, does not prevent the formation of the puffs in bands I-18-C and IV-2-B—those that appear first in the normal sequence—nor does it affect the incorporation of uridine at the puffs. Cycloheximide does, however, abolish the puffs that are scheduled to develop later. After protein synthesis is resumed upon withdrawal of the drug, the pattern of puffing and uridine incorporation is restored in the late-appearing puff regions, and the puffs appear in the same sequence and with the same time intervals as in controls. These observations suggest that protein synthesis is required before late-appearing puffs can arise. A reasonable interpretation of these results, but not the only possible one, is that ecdysone more or less directly activates the genes at bands

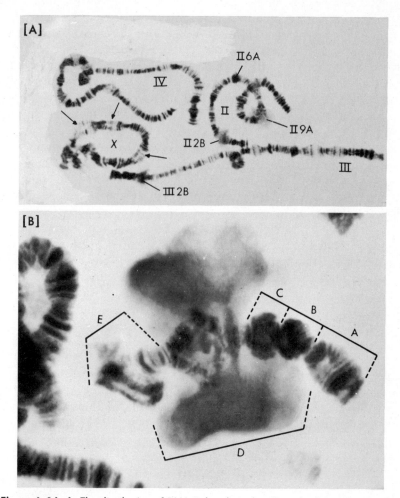

Figure 6·16. A. The distribution of DNA in bands and puffs in the four giant chromosomes of a salivary-gland cell of a larva of the fly *Sciara coprophilia,* as revealed by staining with the Feulgen reagent. The autosomes are identified by roman numerals, the sex chromosome by *X.* This preparation was made from a female larva, and the permanent pairing of homologous chromosomes is shown in the *X* chromosome at points indicated by unlabeled arrows. Labeled arrows direct attention to certain bands that are puffed in chromosomes II and III. **B.** The small chromosome IV of the salivary-gland cell of a larva of *Chironomus thumni* at high magnification, showing puffing of segments *b* and *c* and of the nucleolar region *d.* The puffs are sites of intensive RNA synthesis. The pattern of banding and the dual nature of the chromosome are clearly seen. [**A** courtesy of Dr. Ellen M. Rasch; **B** courtesy of Dr. Hans Laufer.]

I-18-C and IV-2-B, causing them to allow the synthesis of RNA (presumably mRNA) that then encodes for protein synthesis. Subsequent reactions that are of unknown complexity but that depend on prior protein synthesis (possibly initiated by mRNA from the first puffs) then activate the genetic materials at the other loci.

In metamorphosis of the larva of the blowfly *Calliphora,* darkening and hardening of the larval cuticle occur as a response to the action of ecdysone. Essential to the cuticular response is the formation of the hardening agent N-acetyl-dopamine, which is derived from the amino acid tyrosine in a series of chemical steps, one of which is catalyzed by the enzyme dopa decarboxylase. This enzyme appears only at the time puparium formation is scheduled, and its presence is prevented by actinomycin D. This suggests that synthesis of new messenger RNA is required for formation of dopa decarboxylase. In support of this possibility, one finds that radioactively labeled ecdysone injected into the larva is distributed in high proportion to the nuclei of the larval epidermis, where the enzyme is made.

Epigenetic Control of Morphogenesis: The Challenge for Tomorrow

The data just outlined have provided a view of development and its control completely unknown to an earlier generation. We now clearly see the genome as a set of instructions in the form of nucleotide sequences of DNA that specify the sequences of amino acids in proteins. We have recognized the pattern of protein synthesis as being basically what is controlled by the genetic material, and we have learned the pathways whereby this control is exercised. Have we not, then, solved the basic problems of development, so that it is time for scientists to move forward to the conquest of new or less-understood aspects of biological organization, leaving the elucidation of details to the less imaginative? Should we not now turn our attention to, say, neurobiological phenomena, seeking with our new insights a deeper understanding of the operations of the mind—the intellect of the individual and the mass mind of the society?

To be sure, we must be prepared to go ahead as our new insights lead us, but let us not be so naïve as to think that our present knowledge of turnon and turnoff of genetic transcription and translation achieves the objectives of the developmental biologist. The survey of the developmental morphology of the organism and of some morphogenetic mechanisms and principles in preceding chapters should have revealed that there are many levels of organization at which the analysis of development may be legitimately pursued, and that at each level generalizations may be derived that are applicable at that level but have little or no meaning at any other. Consider the limb-forming portion of the embryonic body wall of the chick. Isolated some time before the limb bud actually appears and grown as a graft in an abnormal site, it gives rise to a complete limb. We say that the limb field was determined at the time it was grafted, meaning that its future developmental performance as an appendage had become relatively stabilized long before the appendage itself was formed. But this statement has meaning only at the organ level of organization. It does not explain anything about the properties or developmental commitments of the tissues that comprise the limb-forming area, whether prospective muscle-forming and bone-forming tissues are segregated, or if so, whether their individual developmental assignments are fixed. It certainly does not relate what segments of the genome are being transcribed in individual cells.

In the converse situation, if we were to know at this early stage in the history of the limb-forming area of a bird embryo that the cells were synthesizing proteins *X, Y,* and *Z* at such and such rates, we would not thereby know, necessarily, what portion of the genome would later be transcribed and translated, what tissue architecture would subsequently be created, that an appendage of prescribed definitive form eventually would be established, or if so, that it would function in an appropriate way as a part of a flying animal.

These considerations point up the hierarchical arrangement of organizational levels that emerges during development and illustrate that each level has its appropriate generalizations, which may not serve, or perhaps cannot serve, to predict or describe the nature of events at levels above or below. But for one who would analyze development, it is equally important to keep in mind that the form and function that accrue to any one level of organization must have their foundations and necessarily must emerge automatically—not through operation of some mysterious "life force"—from properties of the system at the lower level.

The concept of the automatic emergence of higher organizational levels from the properties of lower echelons is illustrated by the formation of the protein collagen, the major fibrous component of skin, tendon, ligament, cartilage, and bone. The basic molecular unit of collagen is a chain of amino acids that, looked at from one end, makes a left-handed helix. Three such chains held together by hydrogen bonds and twisted about each other in a right-handed coiled helix comprise a stiff rod about 2,800 Å in length and 15 Å in diameter. This structure has a molecular weight of about 340,000 and is called *tropocollagen;* it is the unit whence collagen fibrils are made (Figure 6·17). Molecules of tropocollagen are synthesized in cells called *fibroblasts* and then emptied into the intercellular spaces where they polymerize in the form of bundles showing a periodic banding with a

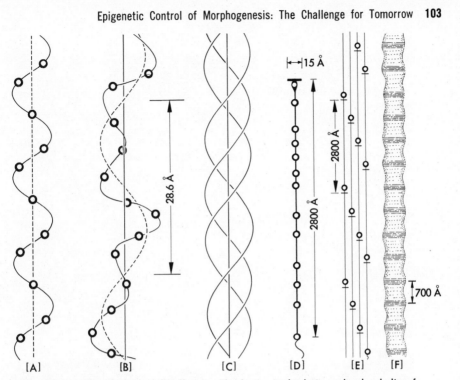

Figure 6·17. The structure of collagen. The basic single-chain molecular helix of collagen is shown in **A**. It is depicted as thrown into a coiled helix in **B**. The three helices of tropocollagen are illustrated in **C**. The tropocollagen molecule is shown in **D** at lower magnification and differentiated as to head and tail ends. At still lower magnification, in **E**, tropocollagen molecules are in parallel array with quarter-length overlap. This leads to the 700-Å spacing seen in the electron micrographs in **F** and in Figure 6·18A. [Adapted from J. Gross, "Collagen," in *Sci. American*, March, 1961, pp. 120–130. Copyright © 1961 by Scientific American, Inc. All rights reserved.]

repeat pattern of about 700 Å. In living systems, these bundles become distributed in various complex arrays, depending on the kind of tissue: in skin they make a dense feltwork; in tendon they form in tight parallel array; in bone they are arranged like the struts and girders of a bridge; and in cartilage they are randomly and sparsely distributed in a matrix of chondroitin sulfate.

It has long been known that if collagen is dissolved in acid, reconstituted fibers appear automatically when the solution is neutralized. The reconstituted fibers show precisely the same periodic banding as do those in the living system. Coming out of solution, the tropocollagen molecules polymerize in parallel array, facing the same direction and overlapping about one-fourth of their length. Heads and tails of the molecules thus meet across the fiber array at about 700-Å intervals, giving the characteristic repeat pattern. The electric charges along the length of the tropocollagen molecules are such that this pattern

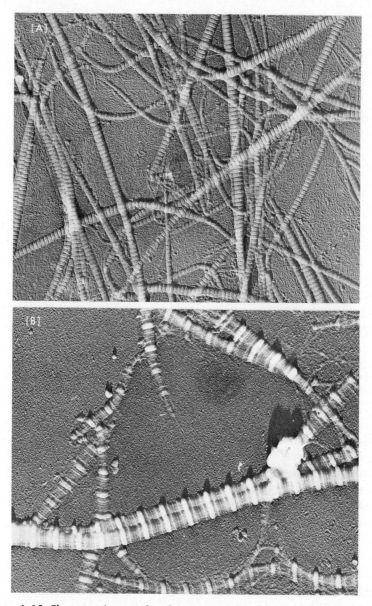

Figure 6·18. Electron micrographs of reconstituted collagen of the swim blad-der of a fish; preparations shadowed with chromium. **A:** The normal period of about 700 Å; prepared by dialyzing the collagen solution against 1 percent NaCl. **B:** Fibrous long spacing of about 2,800 Å; prepared by adding serum acid glycoprotein to the collagen solution and dialyzing against water. [Photographs supplied by Dr. Jerome Gross.]

emerges automatically (Figures 6·17 and 6·18A). But association can be changed to a nonoverlapping one if large negatively charged molecules are added to the solution in which polymerization of the tropocollagen takes place. Thereupon, heads and tails of the tropocollagen line up in register and consequently a periodic banding of 2,800 Å, the length of the molecule, is shown by the fibers (Figure 6·18B).

These considerations show that molecules of tropocollagen, being endowed with a particular set of properties, form structures of a higher level of organization whose new properties are determined by physico-chemical conditions of the milieu. Looking back to a level of organization lower than that of tropocollagen, we note that the component proteins of tropocollagen are produced on ribosomes and then become entwined into a tripartite structure. However it is not the fact that these proteins are synthesized, but rather the properties built into them that determine that they will twist together to form tropocollagen under appropriate conditions within the cell (or in a test-tube system). Automatically, a structure is formed that is of a higher order of organization than its components. Furthermore, that tropocollagen is emptied by the cell into the tissue spaces does not determine that it will form into associations showing a certain repeat pattern. Rather, the attributes of the tropocollagen are such that its molecules will associate or not and make certain repeat patterns or not, depending on the milieu.

In a differentiating tissue, the milieu is created by physical and chemical circumstances issuing from the arrangements and activities of the cells that comprise the tissue. The milieu is varied and complex, depending on the tissue, and it determines the order of emerging collagenous fabrics. Now, indeed, the analysis becomes difficult. What conditions, for example, determine that collagen fibers will arrange themselves in tight parallel array to form a tendon? Or how account for the fact that in tadpole skin they are laid down in stacked parallel plies, each ply having its fibers at right angles to those in the layer above and below (Figure 6·19)?

As yet there has been only limited progress in analyzing the emergence of order at the tissue level from systems at lower levels of organization. A significant beginning has been made, however, in a few studies, one of which concerns the induction of secretory acini in epithelium of the pancreatic rudiment from the eleven-day mouse embryo. If the epithelial portion of the prospective gland is placed in an appropriate culture medium with a thin porous filter separating it from pancreatic mesenchyme, in a few days pancreatic acini are differentiated in the epithelium and are invested with a matrix containing collagenous fibers. Factors diffusing through the filter from the mesen-

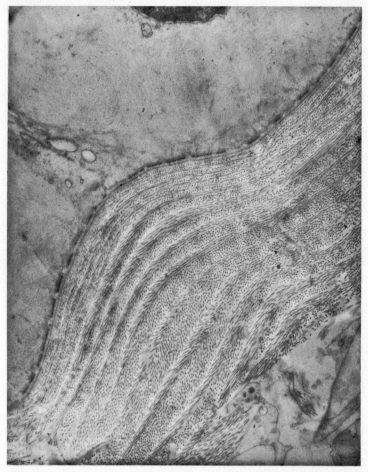

Figure 6·19. Electron micrograph showing the arrangement of collagen fibrils in multiple plies in the skin of the tadpole. The stacked fibers in each ply are ordered at right angles to those in the plies above and below. Approximately thirty-three layers of stacked fibrils separate the epidermis (*upper left*) from the dermis (*lower right*). [Photograph supplied by Dr. Norman Kemp.]

chyme are apparently responsible for the packaging of the epithelial cells into units that then self-differentiate into secretory acini. The origin of the collagenous fibers is particularly interesting in the present context. About forty-eight hours after the culture is made, there appear at the epithelial surface facing the membrane protein fibers having the characteristic 700-Å repeat periodicity of collagen. These are not found within the pores of the filter or on the side facing the mesenchyme. Nevertheless, the source of this collagen-like material is apparently the mesenchyme, for when mesenchyme labeled with the radioactive amino acid proline (proline is incorporated into collagen and hydroxylated to form hydroxyproline) is placed transfilter from the epithelium, a radioactive material moves across the membrane and is deposited on the epithelial side. This material is removed by the hydrolytic enzyme collagenase. Conversely, when epithelium labeled with radioactive proline is combined transfilter with nonlabeled mesenchyme, the pattern in which the label is subsequently distributed does not reflect the location of collagen. Presumably, the formation of a collagenous layer at the feet of the epithelial cells involves the transfer of soluble tropocollagen from the mesenchyme where it is synthesized, through the filter to the epithelial surface that provides the conditions for its polymerization into fiber bundles.

This case is a particularly clear example of the way in which a higher order of complexity may emerge epigenetically from processes carried out at a lower level. It is an artificial case, to be sure, but it indicates the kind of approach that must be undertaken in considering the emergent evolution of new properties at the tissue level from those that occur at the cellular level of organization.

When one proceeds from the tissue level to the organ level, complexities increase. We can possibly see our way clear to deriving a geometric pattern of collagen molecules from the known basic physicochemical properties of the molecule and its environment. But accounting for the geometry that is superimposed on tissues by their integration into organs poses problems of much greater magnitude and complexity. Let us look at the case of a (deceptively) simple organ—the skin of the fowl. In its development the basic interacting tissues comprise the prospective skin dermis (mesoderm) and epidermis, which cooperate to form feather germs in a series of very precise geometric patterns. Relatively early in development, a primitive kind of dermis differentiates in the superficial mesenchyme. It is closely associated with the overlying epidermis and slightly demarcated from the premuscle masses beneath. The origin of a feather in this dermis is first signaled by a condensation in the mesenchyme (Figure 4·6), the dermal papilla. Over this condensation, the epidermis proliferates and forms a conical protrusion whence, eventually, the down feather will arise. This is as far as I shall go in pursuing the developmental history of the feather in this book. What is of interest here is the fact that the dermal papillae arise only in certain regions of the skin, the feather tracts, and that within each tract they form rigidly specific geometric patterns. There first appears a row of dermal condensations, usually running parallel to the head-tail axis of the animal. This is the primary row, or row of origin. Secondary rows arise on either side of the first, the condensations occupying a position corresponding to the spaces between condensations in the primary row. Tertiary and quaternary rows subsequently appear, and the alternating positions of the dorsal

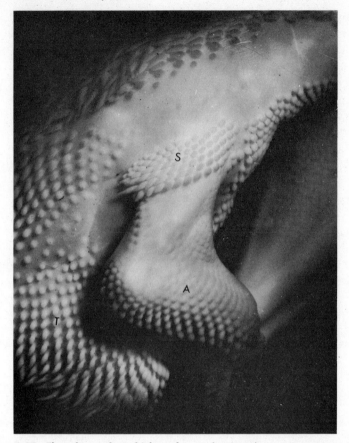

Figure 6·20. The eleven-day chick embryo, showing the precise geometric patterns in which the feather germs are arranged in shoulder (S), alar (A), and thigh (T) tracts.

condensation determine that feather positions will occur at the intersections of diagonal coordinates with longitudinal rows (Figure 6·20).

This very precise geometric relationship of feather positions is maintained throughout the life of the bird, and when the definitive feathers of the adult plumage are formed, they show gradients in structure, growth rate, response to hormones, and so on, along the coordinate axes that define the tract. Thus each feather is a unique structure.

One cannot grow definitive feathers in tissue culture, but one can explant embryonic skin comprising prospective dermis and overlying ectoderm to artificial media that will permit the dermal condensations to form and the feather germs to grow to a respectable size. If, however, the mesodermal portion of the skin is isolated, the dermal condensations do not form; likewise, if skin ectoderm is isolated, it will not proliferate the conical feather outgrowth.

Quite obviously, epigenetically derived properties of ectoderm and mesoderm at the tissue level of organization in prospective skin are such that dermal condensations can occur and that epidermal proliferation can then follow over each condensation; and in each component of the future skin system, these properties are based on activities at the underlying cellular and molecular levels. At this point, however, even knowing that cells of each component are reading out and translating certain instructions—i.e., making certain proteins—does not help to explain the origin of mesodermal condensations and the ectodermal proliferation; much less does it explain the emergence of feather germs in orderly sequence and geometric array. Interpretation of these aspects of morphogenesis requires insights that we seem not to have achieved as yet and that can only be gained through attacks on the problem at multiple levels.

This example sets the scene for issuing the challenge for tomorrow to the student of today. The challenge is to learn to ask of the developing system meaningful questions relative to multiple levels of organization—questions that will clarify the state of the system at each level—and, thereafter, to formulate questions that will reveal the mechanisms whereby the higher order of integration, the higher level of organization, emerges automatically from the preceding level. Only thus can development be understood.

Selected References

GENERAL TEXTS, ESSAYS, AND COLLECTIONS

Balinsky, B. I. *An Introduction to Embryology,* 2d ed., Philadelphia: Saunders, 1965.

Barth, L. G. *Embryology,* rev. ed., New York: Holt, 1953.

Barth, L. J. *Development: Selected Topics,* Reading, Mass.: Addison-Wesley, 1964.

Berrill, N. J. *Growth, Development and Pattern,* San Francisco: Freeman, 1961.

Bonner, J. T. *Morphogenesis: An Essay on Development,* Princeton, N.J.: Princeton, 1952.

Ebert, J. D. *Interacting Systems in Development,* New York: Holt, 1965.

Edds, M. V., Jr. "Animal Morphogenesis," in W. Johnson and W. Steere (eds.), *This Is Life,* New York: Holt, 1962, pp. 271–284.

Grobstein, C. *The Strategy of Life,* San Francisco: Freeman, 1964.

Hamilton, H. L. *Lillie's Development of the Chick,* New York: Holt, 1952.

Nalbandov, A. V. *Reproductive Physiology,* 2d ed., San Francisco: Freeman, 1964.

Patten, B. M. *Foundations of Embryology,* 2d ed., New York: McGraw-Hill, 1964.

Sussman, M. *Growth and Development,* 2d ed., Englewood Cliffs, N.J.: Prentice-Hall, 1964.

Torrey, T. W. *Morphogenesis of the Vertebrates,* New York: Wiley, 1962.

Waddington, C. H. *Principles of Embryology,* New York: Macmillan, 1956.

———. *Principles of Development and Differentiation,* New York: Macmillan, 1966.

Weiss, P. A. *Principles of Development,* New York: Holt, 1939.

Willier, B. H., and J. M. Oppenheimer (eds.). *Foundations of Experimental Embryology,* Englewood Cliffs, N.J.: Prentice-Hall, 1964.

———, et al. (eds.). *Analysis of Development,* Philadelphia: Saunders, 1955.

FERTILIZATION

Austin, C. R. *Fertilization,* Englewood Cliffs, N.J.: Prentice-Hall, 1965.

Colwin, A. L., and L. H. Colwin. "Role of the Gamete Membranes in Fertilization," in M. Locke (ed.), *Cellular Membranes in Development,* New York: Academic, 1964, pp. 233–279.

Monroy, A. *Chemistry and Physiology of Fertilization,* New York: Holt, 1965.

Szollosi, D., and H. Ris. "Observations on Sperm Penetration in the Rat," *J. Biophys. Biochem. Cytol.,* 10:275–283, 1961.

Tyler, A., et al. *The Beginnings of Embryonic Development,* Washington, D.C.: American Association for the Advancement of Science, 1957.

CONSTRUCTION OF TISSUES AND ORGANS

DeHaan, R. L., and H. Ursprung (eds.). *Organogenesis,* New York: Holt, 1965.

Moscona, A. A. "Patterns and Mechanisms of Tissue Reconstruction from Dissociated Cells," in D. Rudnick (ed.), *Developing Cell Systems and Their Control,* New York: Ronald, 1960, pp. 45–70.

Saxen, L., and S. Toivonen. *Primary Embryonic Induction,* London: Logos Press, 1962.

Spemann, H. *Embryonic Development and Induction,* New Haven, Conn.: Yale, 1938.

Steinberg, M. S. "The Problem of Adhesive Selectivity in Cellular Interactions," in M. Locke (ed.), *Cellular Membranes in Development,* New York: Academic, 1964, pp. 321–366.

NUCLEIC ACIDS AND THE BIOSYNTHESIS OF MACROMOLECULES

Barry, J. M. *Molecular Biology: Genes and the Chemical Control of Living Cells,* Englewood Cliffs, N.J.: Prentice-Hall, 1964.

Crick, F. H. C. "The Genetic Code," *Sci. American,* October, 1962, pp. 66–74.

———. "The Genetic Code: III," *Sci. American,* October, 1966, pp. 55–62.

Hartman, P. E., and S. R. Suskind. *Gene Action,* Englewood Cliffs, N.J.: Prentice-Hall, 1965.

Holley, R. W. "The Nucleotide Sequence of a Nucleic Acid," *Sci. American,* February, 1966, pp. 30–39.

Hurwitz, J., and J. J. Furth. "Messenger RNA," *Sci. American,* February, 1962, pp. 41–49.

Ingram, V. W. *The Biosynthesis of Macromolecules,* New York: W. A. Benjamin, Inc., 1965.

Nirenberg, M. W. "The Genetic Code: II," *Sci. American,* March, 1963, pp. 80–94.

Rich, A. "Polyribosomes," *Sci. American,* December, 1963, pp. 44–53.

Steiner, R. F. *The Chemical Foundations of Molecular Biology,* Princeton, N.J.: Van Nostrand, 1965.

Watson, J. D. *Molecular Biology of the Gene,* New York: W. A. Benjamin, Inc., 1965.

GENETIC CONTROL OF DEVELOPMENTAL EVENTS

Beerman, W., and U. Clever. "Chromosome Puffs," *Sci. American,* April, 1964, pp. 50–58.

Bell, E. (ed.). *Molecular and Cellular Aspects of Development,* New York: Harper & Row, 1965.

Bonner, J. M. *The Molecular Biology of Development,* London: Oxford, 1965.

Brown, D. D., and E. Littna. "Absence of Ribosomal RNA Synthesis in the Anucleolate Mutant of *Xenopus laevis,*" *Proc. Nat. Acad. of Sci. U.S.,* 51: 139–146, 1964.

Davidson, E. H. "Hormones and Genes," *Sci. American,* June, 1965, pp. 36–45.

Gibor, A. "Acetabularia: A Useful Giant Cell," *Sci. American,* November, 1966, pp. 118–124.

Gross, P. R., and G. H. Cousineau. "Macromolecule Synthesis and the Influence of Actinomycin on Early Development," *Exptl. Cell Research,* 33:368–395, 1964.

Gurdon, J. B. "Nuclear Transplantation in Amphibia and the Importance of Stable Nuclear Changes in Promoting Cellular Differentiation," *Quart. Rev. Biol.,* 38:54–78, 1963.

King, J. T., and R. Briggs. "Changes in the Nuclei of Differentiating Gastrula Cells, as Demonstrated by Nuclear Transplantation," *Proc. Nat. Acad. Sci. U.S.,* 41:321–325, 1955.

Index

(A + G) / (C + T) ratios, 80
Acetabularia, nuclear transplantation in, 71, 72
Acrosome, 8, 9, 14–18
Actinomycin D, and enzyme production, 92, 97, 101
Activating enzymes, 84, 85, 95
Adenine, in deoxyribose nucleic acid, 76, 78
Amblystoma maculatum, developmental stages, 42
Amino acids, activation of, 84
    assembly in polypeptides, 86–89
    attachment to sRNA, 84, 85
    codons for, 82, 83
    incorporation stimulated at fertilization, 94
Amino acyl synthetase (*see* Activating enzyme)
Amphibian egg, 13
    cleavage, 27, 28
    regulative development of, 69
Amphibian embryo, determination of nervous system, 57, 58
    developmental stages, 28, 29, 41, 43
    fate maps, 30
    gastrulation, 30–32
Animal field, 64
    (*See also* Morphogenetic field)
Animal pole, 11–13
Animal-vegetal axis, 12, 22
Anticodon, definition, 84
Appendages, origin of, 29, 47, 48
Archenteron, 24–32, 57–58
Auditory capsule, induction of, 59
Axolotl, nuclear transplantation in, 73, 74

Balbiani rings (*see* Puffs)
Base pairs, in DNA double helix, 79, 81
Beta galactosidase, mRNA for, 86
Bird egg, 12, 13
    cleavage and gastrulation, 32–36
    germ layer formation, 33, 34
    (*See also* Chick embryo; Duck embryo)

Blastocoele, 22, 24, 28, 30, 31
Blastocyst, 37, 38
Blastoderm, 32
Blastodisc, 13
Blastomeres, 22
    of *Crepidula,* 25, 26
    of *Ilyanassa,* 68
    of sea urchin, 22–24
    of *Styela,* 67, 68
Blastopore, 30, 31
    dorsal lip, 30
    invagination of mesoderm through, 45
Blastula, 22
    amphibian, 28, 29
Brain, origin of, 28, 41
    inductions by, 58, 59

Calliphora, ecdysone effects on cuticle, 101
Cells, affinities between, 53–55
    cartilage, and synthesis of chondroitin sulfate, 87
    death of, 47, 48
    mobility of, 53
    of neural crest, 43, 44
    sorting behavior of, 55
Cellular death, morphogenetic role, 47, 48
Chick embryo, appendages, development of, 47, 48
    developmental stages, 42, 56
    eye field, 66
    feathers, origin of, 46
    gastrulation (*see* Bird egg)
    glutamine synthetase in, 97
    heart, origin of, 48
    lens formation in, 93
    mesodermal derivatives, 46
    morphogenetic fields of, 48, 65, 66
    relationships of germ layers, 46
    (*See also* Appendages; Leg bud; Limb bud; Wing bud)
Chironomus, chromosomal puffs in, 99, 100
Chromosomes, and nucleolar organizers, 95

as bearers of genes, 70, 71
of salivary glands, 99, 100
Ciona egg, loss of developmental plasticity in, 69
Cleavage, in various organisms, 21–39
Codons, definition, 82
of messenger RNA, 83, 85, 89
64 possible, 82, 83
Collagen, effect on muscle differentiation, 97, 98
reconstitution of, 103
structure of, 102–105
trans-filter deposition of, 105, 106
Competence, 59
Conklin, E. G., 25, 26
Cornea, origin of, 45, 59
Cortical alveoli, 15
Cranial nerves, origin of, 43, 44
Crayfish egg, yolk synthesis in, 10, 11
Crepidula egg, cleavage and gastrulation of, 25–27
Cytosine, in deoxyribose nucleic acid, 76–78

Deoxyribose nucleic acid (DNA), as genetic language, 80, 81
base composition and pairing in, 78–80
copying of by RNA, 81, 82
inhibited by actinomycin D, 92
double helical structure of, 79, 80, 92
nucleotide building blocks of, 76–80
time of synthesis in cell cycle, 5
Determination, 56, 57
Development, definition, 1
stages in, of amphibian embryo, 28, 41, 43
of chick embryo, 42, 56
Differentiation, of cartilage, 97
of collagenous tissues, 105–107
concept of, 52, 55
dependent (*see* Induction)
discreteness of, 52
of muscle, in presence of collagen, 97
stability of, 53
DNA (*see* Deoxyribose nucleic acid)
Dorsal lip of blastopore, 30, 58
Drosophila, eye pigments of, 74, 75
Duck embryo, gastrulation in, 31

Ecdysone, and chromosomal puffing, 99–101
Ectoderm, competence for lens induction in, 59
definition, 21
and formation of eye, 43
genetic limitations of inductive response in, 59, 60
induction of neural tube in, 57–59
morphogenesis of, 41
role in limb development, 61–63
Egg, animal-vegetal axis of, 12
centrolecithal, 11, 12
cortical reaction of, 14–18
isolecithal, 11, 12

membranes of, 11, 12
mosaic, 67–69
penetration by sperm, 16
plasma membrane of, 15
preformed organization, in amphibian, 27
in *Styela,* 67, 68
regulative, 69
ripeness of, 14
telolecithal, 10, 12
yolk distribution in, 10–12
(*See also* Ovum; Oöcyte)
Endoderm, definition, 21
morphogenesis of, 49, 50
and origin of primordial germ cells, 49, 50
primary, 38
substrate for migration of heart-forming cells, 48
Epidermis, role in feather formation, 107–108
Epigenesis, 67–70
Eye, morphogenetic field of, 66
Eye pigments, origin in *Drosophila,* 74, 75
Eyelids, origin of, 45

Fate maps, of amphibian blastula, 30
Feathers, origin of, 45, 46, 107
Fertilization, 14–18
and loss of developmental plasticity, 69
Fields, morphogenetic (*see* Morphogenetic fields)
Frog, tadpole of, 11
skin of, 106
Frog embryo, oral ectoderm and mouth parts of, 60, 61
Frog egg, 13
cleavage of, 27, 28
(*See also* Amphibian egg; Urodele egg)

Gametes, origin of, 4–14
Gastrula, definition, 22
(*See also* Gastrulation)
Gastrulation, and ribosome synthesis, 95
in various organisms, 30–39
Genes, activation by ecdysone, 99–101
activation by hormones, 98–101
affecting biochemical reactions, 73–75
as controllers of differentiation, 3, 71–78
copying of by RNA, 80–82
for sickle-cell anemia, 75
Genetic code, amino acids and, 83
and nucleotide base sequences, 80–83
Genetic limitations of inductive response, feather structure, 61
mouthparts of amphibians, 61
principle of, 60, 61
Genome, coding for protein synthesis by, 89
definition, 2
frequency of transcription of, 92

Genome (*continued*)
  presence of in all cells, 89, 90
  as set of instructions, 101
  transcription of by RNA, 80, 82
    control by hormones, 99
    control by milieu, 99, 100
Germ layers, definition, 21
  origin of, 19–39
Germ cells, definition, 4
  primordial, 4
    origin and migration of, 49, 50
Germinal vesicle, 10
Glutamine synthetase, 97
Gonial cells, 4–6
Gonads, migration of primordial germ
    cells to, 49, 50
  as sites of gamete formation, 4
Gray crescent, amphibian, 27–28
  of *Styela*, 67
  transplantation of, 58
Guanine, in deoxyribose nucleic acid,
    76–78

Heart, boiled, as inductor of lens, 59
  morphogenetic field of, 48
  origin of, 48, 49
Heart cells, invagination through primi-
    tive streak, 34, 36
  migration of, 48
  tissue affinities of, 55
Hela cells, messenger RNA of, half-life
    of, 72
Hemoglobin, length of messenger RNA,
    86
  in sickle-cell anemia, 75
Hen's egg, 13
  (*See also* Bird egg; Chick embryo;
    Duck embryo)
Hensen's node, 34–37
Histones, 91
Homologous chromosomes, pairing in
    meiosis, 6, 7
Hormones, and genetic transcription,
    98–101
Human embryo, cleavage, gastrulation,
    and implantation of, 36–39
Hydrocortisone, effects on enzyme syn-
    thesis, 98
Hydrogen bonds, in DNA base pairs, 79,
    80

Ilyanassa egg, cleavage in, 68
Implantation, of primate embryo, 38
Induction, 57–63
  definition, 51, 57
  genetic limitation of response, 60–61
  hierarchy of, 58
  of kidney tubules, 60
  of nervous system, 57, 58
  by nonliving inductors, 59, 60
  of pancreatic acini, 105
  principle of, 51, 57
  of sense organs, 59
  specificity of, 59, 60
Insect egg, yolk accumulation in, 11

Iris, regeneration of lens from, 53, 90

Jelly, of frog egg, 12
  release of precursor in *Nereis*, 15

Kidney tubules, induction of, 60

Leg bud, of chick embryo, 42
  morphogenesis of, 46–48
  (*See also* Appendages; Wing bud; Leg
    bud)
Lens, induction of, 59
  long-lived messenger RNA in, 93
  origin of, 43, 45
  protein synthesis in, 93
  regeneration of, 53, 90
Limb bud, origin of, 47
  (*See also* Appendages; Leg bud; Wing
    bud)
Lithium ion (Li++), and inhibition of
    invagination, 57
  role in extending vegetal field, 64
Liver, boiled, as inductor of lens, 59
  cells of, relative affinities, 55

Macromeres, of *Crepidula*, 26, 28
  of sea urchin egg, 23, 24
  prospective fate of, 25
Mammalian egg, yolk distribution in, 11
Mammalian embryo, development of,
    37–39
Meiosis, 6–8
Melanoblasts, origin, 44
Mesoderm, definition, 21
  derivatives of, 28, 29
  invagination, in amphibian embryo,
    30–31
    in chick embryo, 33–35
  in origin of appendages, 29, 56, 61–63
  origin from 4d-cell, 27
Mesomeres, of sea urchin embryo, 23, 24
Messenger RNA, attachment to ribo-
    somes, 85, 87
  codons of, 89
  copying of DNA by, 81
  half-life of, 92
  length of, 86
  in polyribosomes, 88
  in protein synthesis, 86–89
  synthesis, hormonal control of, 91
Micromeres, of *Crepidula*, 26
  of sea urchin, production during cleav-
    age, 25
  prospective fate of, 24, 64
Mitosis, in gonial cells, 4, 5
Mitotic spindle, position of, during am-
    phibian cleavage, 27, 28
  in spirally cleaving eggs, 25, 26
  in sea urchin eggs, 23
Morphogenesis, definition of, 1
Morphogenetic field, center of, 64
  chordamesoderm, 63
    localization in gray crescent, 69
  definition, 63
  extension of properties, 66

of eye, 66
  fate maps for, of amphibian blastula,
    30
    of eye, 66
    of heart, 48
  fusion of, 65
  gradients in, 65
  of heart, 48, 66
  heteropolarity of, 65
  of limb, 63
  and Li^{++}, 64
  regulation in, 65
  of sea urchin egg, 64, 65
Morula, 37
Muscle, differentiation affected by colla-
    gen, 97, 98

Nasal grooves, placodal origin of, 43
Nereis, fertilization in, 15–17
Nervous system, induction of, 57–59
  origin, 19, 21, 41, 43, 67
Neural crest, derivatives of, 43
  migration of cells from, 43, 44
  origin from neural folds, 41
Neural plate, origin from ectoderm, 41
Neurospora, 75
Neurula, of amphibian, 28, 29
Notochord, of amphibian, 28, 29, 43
  of chick embryo, 34
  origin of, 31, 46, 67
  of *Styela,* 67
Nuclear transplantation, in *Acetabu-
    laria,* 71, 72
  in axolotl, 73, 74
  and nucleolar structure, 96
  in *Rana pipiens,* 73, 90
  in *Xenopus,* 90, 96
Nucleolus, site of ribosomal synthesis, 95
  of *Xenopus* mutant, 95, 96
Nucleotides, as building blocks of DNA,
    76–80
  as components of RNA, 80, 81
Nucleus, as determiner of developmental
    events, 71
  preformed organization in, 69, 70

Oöcyte, maturation spindles of, 13
  nucleus of, 10
Oögenesis, definition, 8
Oöplasm, effects on nucleolus, 96
  organization of, in amphibian egg, 27
    in *Ilyanassa* egg, 68
    in *Styela* egg, 67, 68
Optic vesicle, effects of extirpating, 59
  origin of, 43, 45
Organization center, 58
Organizer (*See* Organization center)
Ovum, maturation of, 12–14

Peptide bonds, formation on ribosomes,
    86
Perivitelline space, origin at fertilization,
    15, 16
Pigeon egg, cleavage of, 32
Placodes, sensory, 43–45

Polar bodies, 11, 13, 28
Polypeptides, synthesis of, 86–89
Polysomes (*See* Polyribosomes)
Polyribosomes, 86–88
Polyspermy, 17, 18
Polyuridilic acid (poly U), 94, 95
Preformation, 67–70
Primary mesenchyme, of sea urchin, 23,
    24
Primate embryo, development of, 36–
    39
Primitive groove, 33, 34
Primitive pit, 33
Primitive streak, of bird embryo, 33–36,
    42
    invagination through, 36, 42
    as related to eye field, 66
    as related to heart field, 48
  regression of, in bird embryo, 34–36
    in primate embryo, 39
Primordial germ cells, origin and mi-
    gration of, 49, 50
Proerythrocyte (*See* Reticulocyte)
Proline, incorporation into collagen, 106
Pronuclei, union of, 18, Frontispiece
Pronucleus, female, 13
Pronucleus, male, 18
Prospective fate, of parts of urodele
    blastula, 30
  of sea urchin blastomeres, 24, 25
Protein, in structure of enzymes, 73
  synthesis of, 86–89
    in absence of mRNA synthesis, 92
    control of during development, 90–
      100
    and incorporation of radioactivity,
      94
    initiation of, 86
    resumption   after   cycloheximide
      treatment, 99
Puffs, chromosomal, ecdysone and, 99–
    101
  RNA synthesis in, 100
Puromycin, and synthesis of glutamine
    synthetase, 97
Purines, bases in nucleotides, 76–81
Pyrimidines, bases in nucleotides, 76–81

Rana pipiens, nuclear transplantation in,
    73, 90
Reciprocal action, principle of, 61
Reticulocyte, half-life of mRNA in, 92
  hemoglobin synthesis in, 92
Ribose nucleic acid (RNA), as tem-
    plate, 86–90
  base composition of, 79–80
  nucleotide building blocks of, 80–81
  role in protein synthesis, 86–89
  synthesis on DNA template
    as affected by histones, 91
    inhibition of, 91
  (*See also* Messenger RNA; Ribosome)
Ribosomal RNA, persistence of, 96
  synthesis determined by cytoplasm,
    95–97

Ribosome, amino acid binding sites on, 85, 87
  assembly site for protein synthesis, 84
  attachment of mRNA, 85, 87
  molecular weight of subunits of, 85
  organization in polyribosomes, 86, 88
  of unfertilized egg, 94
RNA polymerase, 81, 82
  access to DNA, 91
  action blocked, 92

Salamander, response of ectoderm to anuran inductors, 60, 61
Sciara coprophilia, chromosomal puffs in, 100
Sea urchin egg, cleavage and gastrulation of, 22–24
  fertilization of, 94
  protein synthesis in, 94
Sea urchin larvae, 24
Sickle-cell anemia, 75
Soluble RNA (sRNA), alanine-specific, 83, 84
  methylation of bases of, 84
  role in translation. 82–85
  specificity of base sequences of, 82, 84
  stimulation of protein synthesis by, 95
  structure of, 84
Somites, 46, 47
Specificity of cellular association, 53
Sperm, activation of, 14, 16
  approach to egg, 16
  components of, 8, 9
  engulfment by fertilization cone, 16, 17
  nucleus of, 17
  plasma membrane continuous with egg membrane, 17
  preformed structures in, 67
Spermatogenesis, 8
Spiral cleavage, 18
Spisula, polyribosomes of, 88
Styela egg, cleavage of, 67, 68
  organ-forming plasms of, 67, 68

Tadpole, collagen plies in skin of, 106
  of frog, 11

Template RNA (*See* Messenger RNA)
Tetrads, in meiosis, 6–7
  in primary oöcyte, 13
Thymine, in deoxyribose nucleic acid, 76–78
Trophoblast, 38
Tropocollagen, 102–105
Tryptophane, in synthesis of *Drosophila* eye pigment, 74
Tryptophane pyrollase, hormonal control of synthesis, 98
Tyrosine, as precursor of N-acetyl-dopamine, 101

Uracil, in nucleotides of RNA, 80
Uridine, incorporation into puffs, 99
  incorporation into RNA, 92
Urodele embryo, developmental stages of, 42
  tissue affinities in, 54
  (*See also* Amphibian embryo)
Uterus, implantation of embryo in, 38

Vegetal field, of sea urchin egg, 64
Vegetal pole, 12
Vitelline membrane, changes at fertilization, 15, 16
  of chick, 13
  of frog, 13
  of *Nereis,* 15, 16

Wing bud, induction of outgrowth, 61, 62
  self-differentiation of, 56
  (*See also* Appendages; Leg bud)
Wound healing, tissue affinities in, 54

Xenopus, nuclear transplantation in, 90, 96
  nucleolar mutants of, 95, 96

Yolk, definition, 10
  distribution in eggs, 10–13, 22
Yolk sac, in fish, 11
  primary, of mammal, 38

Zygote, of *Acetabularia,* 71
  definition, 1
  genes of, 2